The S
of the Novels and Selected Writings
of Daniel Defoe

ROBINSON CRUSOE

Volume I

The Frontispiece to the first edition of "The Life and
Strange Surprizing Adventures of Robinson Crusoe"
(1719)

The Life & Strange Surprizing

ADVENTURES of
ROBINSON
CRUSOE

Of *YORK*, MARINER

Who lived Eight and Twenty Years, all alone in an
un-inhabited Island on the Coaſt of AMERICA,
near the Mouth of the Great River of Oroonoque;

Having been caſt on Shore by Shipwreck, wherein
all the Men perished but himself.

WITH an Account how he was at laſt as ſtrangely
deliver'd by PYRATES.

Written by Himself

Volume I

OXFORD: BASIL BLACKWELL
Publisher to the SHAKESPEARE HEAD PRESS
of STRATFORD-UPON-AVON
1927

FIRST PUBLISHED BY THE
SHAKESPEARE HEAD PRESS IN 1927
REPRINTED IN GREAT BRITAIN BY
PHOTO OFFSET 1974 BY
WILLIAM CLOWES & SONS, LIMITED,
LONDON, BECCLES AND COLCHESTER

ISBN 0 900659 18 1

THE LIFE AND STRANGE SURPRIZING AD-
VENTURES OF *ROBINSON CRUSOE*, OF
YORK, MARINER: Who lived Eight and Twenty
Years all alone in an un-inhabited Island on the Coaſt of
AMERICA, near the Mouth of the Great River of
Oroonoque; Having been caſt on Shore by Shipwreck,
wherein all the Men perished but himself. WITH an Ac-
count how he was at laſt as ſtrangely deliver'd by
PYRATES. *Written by Himself.* [Device] *L O N D O N:*
Printed for W. TAYLOR at the *Ship* in *Pater-Noſter-
Row.* MDCCXIX.

THE FARTHER ADVENTURES OF *ROBINSON
C R U S O E*; Being the Second and Laſt Part OF HIS
LIFE, And of the STRANGE SURPRIZING ACCOUNTS
of his TRAVELS Round three Parts of the Globe. *Written
by Himself.* To which is added a Map of the World, in
which is Delineated the Voyages of *R O B I N S O N
C R U S O E.* [Device] *L O N D O N :* Printed for W.
TAYLOR at the *Ship* in *Pater-Noſter-Row.* MDCCXIX.

'The Life and . . . Adventures' *was firſt published on
April* 25*th,* 1719, *and* 'The Farther Adventures' *on Auguſt*
20*th in the same year, each in a single octavo volume; they are
re-printed in three volumes in the present edition. The
'Serious Reflections . . . of* Robinson Crusoe' (*August* 6*th,*
1720) *is not here reprinted.*
    The Bibliography of Robinson Crusoe *is complex, &
may be ſtudied in detail in the valuable monograph* 'The
Printing of Robinson Crusoe' *by* H. C. Hutchins
(Columbia University Press, 1925) *on which the following
note is based. While the sheets of* 'The Life and . . . Adventures' *were going through the press, certain miſtakes were
correɗed, in the Preface and on one page of the text, and at the*

same time other mistakes were introduced; but during the binding, corrected and uncorrected sheets were treated indiscriminately, with the result that copies of the book may contain partly the earlier (uncorrected) sheets, and partly the later.

There are thus variant readings in different copies, & these have caused much difficulty to Bibliographers; but all these copies are identifiable as being of the first edition, of which there was only one complete printing, or 'issue.'

The second edition appeared on May 12th, the third (of which there were two separate printings) on June 6th, and the fourth on August 8th, 1719.

The present edition is reprinted from the British Museum *copy (c.30.f.6) of the first edition, compared with the third edition, in which certain alterations were included. The 'Errata' given in a list at the end of the first edition have been incorporated in the text.*

The first edition of 'The Farther Adventures' *presents similar difficulties; but in this case in addition to variant readings in the first 'issue,' there is a second 'issue'—which introduces further variations; both were published together, & form the first 'edition.'*

An advertisement of the Fourth edition of 'The Life and ... Adventures' *& the attack on* Cox's ' Amsterdam Coffee-House' *abridgment (see page* viii *below) appear in the second 'issue,' but not in the first.*

The publishers are indebted to the courtesy of Mrs. Clement Shorter *for the loan of her valuable copy of the second 'issue' from which the present edition has been printed. It has been compared in proof with a copy of the first 'issue' (250.x.8) in the* Bodleian Library.

LIST OF ILLUSTRATIONS

NOTE.—With the exception of the Frontispiece and the Map of the World (see Volume II), the twelve plates reproduced in these volumes appeared originally in the 6th edition of "The Life and ... Adventures," and the 3rd edition of "The Farther Adventures." They were republished in 1726 by W. Mears and T. Woodward in a uniform 12mo edition in two volumes, which constitute the 7th edition of "The Life and ... Adventures" and the 5th edition of "The Farther Adventures." The present reproductions have been made from the British Museum copy of this 12mo edition.

THE PREFACE.

[*To* THE LIFE AND STRANGE SURPRIZING ADVENTURES OF ROBINSON CRUSOE]

IF ever the Story of any private Man's Adventures in the World were worth making Publick, and were acceptable when Publish'd, the Editor of this Account thinks this will be so.

The Wonders of this Man's Life exceed all that (he thinks) is to be found extant; the Life of one Man being scarce capable of a greater Variety.

The Story is told with Modesty, with Seriousness, and with a religious Application of Events to the Uses to which wise Men always apply them (viz.) to the Instruction of others by this Example, and to justify and honour the Wisdom of Providence in all the Variety of our Circumstances, let them happen how they will.

The Editor believes the thing to be a just History of Fact; neither is there any Appearance of Fiction in it: And however thinks, because all such things are dispatch'd,*that the Improvement of it, as well to the Diversion, as to the Instruction of the Reader, will be the same; and as such, he thinks, without farther Compliment to the World, he does them a great Service in the Publication.

[*To* THE FARTHER ADVENTURES OF ROBINSON CRUSOE]

THE Success the former Part of this Work has met with in the World, has yet been no other than is acknowledg'd to be due to the surprising Variety of the Subject, and to the agreeable Manner of the Performance.

All the Endeavours of envious People to reproach it with

*All Editions except the first two read *disputed*.

being a Romance, to search it for Errors in Geography, Incon-
sistency in the Relation, and Contradictions in the Fact, have
proved abortive, and as impotent as malicious.

The just Application of every Incident, the religious and
useful Inferences drawn from every Part, are so many Testi-
monies to the good Design of making it publick, and must legiti-
mate all the Part that may be call'd Invention, or Parable in
the Story.

The Second Part, if the Editor's Opinion may pass, is (con-
trary to the Usage of Second Parts,) every Way as entertain-
ing as the First, contains as strange and surprising Incidents,
and as great a Variety of them; nor is the Application less seri-
ous, or suitable; and doubtless will, to the sober, as well as in-
genious Reader, be every way as profitable and diverting; and
this makes the abridging this Work, as scandalous, as it is
knavish and ridiculous; seeing, while to shorten the Book, that
they may seem to reduce the Value, they strip it of all those Re-
flections, as well religious as moral, which are not only the
greatest Beautys of the Work, but are calculated for the infinite
Advantage of the Reader.

By this they leave the Work naked of its brightest Orna-
ments; and if they would, at the same Time pretend, that the
Author has supply'd the Story out of his Invention, they take
from it the Improvement, which alone recommends that In-
vention to wise and good Men.

The Injury these Men do the Proprietor of this Work, is a
Practice all honest Men abhor; and he believes he may chal-
lenge them to shew the Difference between that and Robbing
on the Highway, or Breaking open a House.

If they can't shew any Difference in the Crime, they will
find it hard to shew why there should be any Difference in the
Punishment: And he will answer for it, that nothing shall be
wanting on his Part, to do them Justice.

Just Published, the 4th Edition

O F the Life and ſtrange surprising Adventures of
R O B I N S O N   C R U S O E, of *York*, Mariner: Who
lived eight and twenty Years all alone in an un-inha-
bited Island on the Coaſt of *America*, near the Mouth of
the Great River *Oroonoque*; having been caſt on Shore by
Shipwreck, wherein all the Men perished but himself.
With an Account how he was at laſt as ſtrangely deliver'd
by Pyrates. *Written by himself*. To this Edition is added a
Map of the World, in which is Delineated the Voyages of
R O B I N S O N   C R U S O E. Printed for W. Taylor, at the
Ship in *Pater-Noſter-Row*.

N.B. The pretended Abridgment of this Book, clan-
deſtinely Printed for *T. Cox*, at the *Amſterdam* Coffee-
House, consiſts only of some scatter'd Passages incohe-
rently tacked together; wherein the Author's Sense
throughout is wholly miſtaken, the Matters of Faćt, mis-
represented, and the Moral Reflećtions misapplied. It's
hop'd the Publick will not give Encouragement to so
base a Praćtice, the Proprietor intending to Prosecute the
Venders according to Law.

[Note. *This pirated abridgment was published about
August 1st, 1729, and was sold at Two Shillings in order
to compete with the genuine edition, which coſt Five Shillings.
Taylor, the publisher of the genuine edition carried out his
threat, and began proceedings for the protection of his copyright.
Cox replied, threatening to disclose certain secrets, and making
insinuations againſt the Author. The episode is obscure, but
the legal proceedings were withdrawn.*]

THE LIFE AND ADVENTURES OF ROBINSON CRUSOE,

&c.

I WAS born in the Year 1632, in the City of *York*, of a good Family, tho' not of that Country, my Father being a Foreigner of *Bremen*, who settled firſt at *Hull*: He got a good Eſtate by Merchandise, and leaving off his Trade, lived afterward at *York*, from whence he had married my Mother, whose Relations were named *Robinson*, a very good Family in that Country, and from whom I was called *Robinson Kreutznaer*; but by the usual Corruption of Words in *England*, we are now called, nay we call our selves, and write our Name *Crusoe*, and so my Companions always call'd me.

I had two elder Brothers, one of which was Lieutenant Collonel to an *English* Regiment of Foot in *Flanders*, formerly commanded by the famous Coll. *Lockhart*, and was killed at the Battle near *Dunkirk* againſt the *Spaniards*: What became of my second Brother I never knew any more than my Father or Mother did know what was become of me.

Being the third Son of the Family, and not bred to any Trade, my Head began to be fill'd very early with rambling Thoughts: My Father, who was very ancient, had given me a competent Share of Learning, as far as House-Education, and a Country Free-School generally goes, and design'd me for the Law; but I would be satisfied with nothing but going to Sea, and my Inclination to this led me so strongly against the Will, nay, the Commands of my Father, and against all the Entreaties and Persuasions of my Mother, and other Friends, that there seem'd to be something fatal in that Propension of Nature tending directly to the Life of Misery which was to befal me.

My Father, a wise and grave Man, gave me serious and excellent Counsel against what he foresaw was my Design. He call'd me one Morning into his Chamber, where he was confined by the Gout, and expostulated very warmly with me upon this Subject: He ask'd me what Reasons more than a meer wandring Inclination I had for leaving my Father's House and my native Country, where I might be well introduced, and had a Prospect of raising my Fortune by Application and Industry, with a Life of Ease and Pleasure. He told me it was for Men of desperate Fortunes on one Hand, or of aspiring, superior Fortune on the other, who went abroad upon Adventures, to rise by Enterprize, and make themselves famous in Undertakings of a Nature out of the common Road; that these things were all either too far above me, or too far below me; that mine was the middle State, or what might be called the upper Station of *Low Life*, which he had found by long Experience was the best State in the World, the most suited to human Happiness, not exposed to the Miseries and Hardships, the Labour and Sufferings of the mechanick Part of Mankind, and not embarass'd with the Pride, Luxury, Ambition and Envy of the upper Part of Mankind. He told me, I might judge of the Happiness of this State, by this one thing, *viz*. That this was the State of Life which all other People envied, that Kings have frequently lamented the miser-

able Consequences of being born to great things, and
wish'd they had been placed in the Middle of the two
Extremes, between the Mean and the Great; that the
wise Man gave his Testimony to this as the just Standard
of true Felicity, when he prayed to have neither Poverty
or Riches.

He bid me observe it, and I should always find, that
the Calamities of Life were shared among the upper and
lower Part of Mankind; but that the middle Station had
the fewest Disasters, and was not expos'd to so many
Vicissitudes as the higher or lower Part of Mankind;
nay, they were not subjected to so many Distempers and
Uneasinesses either of Body or Mind, as those were who,
by vicious Living, Luxury and Extravagancies on one
Hand, or by hard Labour, Want of Necessaries, and
mean or insufficient Diet on the other Hand, bring Distempers upon themselves by the natural Consequences
of their Way of Living; *That* the middle Station of Life
was calculated for all kind of Vertues and all kinds of En-
joyments; that Peace and Plenty were the Hand-maids
of a middle Fortune; that Temperance, Moderation,
Quietness, Health, Society, all agreeable Diversions, and
all desirable Pleasures, were the Blessings attending the
middle Station of Life; that this Way Men went silently
and smoothly thro' the World, and comfortably out of it,
not embarass'd with the Labours of the Hands or of the
Head, not sold to the Life of Slavery for daily Bread, or
harrast with perplex'd Circumstances, which rob the
Soul of Peace, and the Body of Rest; not enrag'd with the
Passion of Envy, or secret burning Lust of Ambition for
great things; but in easy Circumstances sliding gently
thro' the World, and sensibly tasting the Sweets of living, without the bitter, feeling that they are happy, and

learning by every Day's Experience to know it more sensibly.

After this, he press'd me earneſtly, and in the moſt affectionate manner, not to play the young Man, not to precipitate my self into Miseries which Nature and the Station of Life I was born in, seem'd to have provided againſt; that I was under no Necessity of seeking my Bread; that he would do well for me, and endeavour to enter me fairly into the Station of Life which he had been juſt recommending to me; and that if I was not very easy and happy in the World, it muſt be my meer Fate or Fault that muſt hinder it, and that he should have nothing to answer for, having thus discharg'd his Duty in warning me againſt Measures which he knew would be to my Hurt: In a word, that as he would do very kind things for me if I would ſtay and settle at Home as he directed, so he would not have so much Hand in my Misfortunes, as to give me any Encouragement to go away: And to close all, he told me I had my elder Brother for an Example, to whom he had used the same earneſt Perswasions to keep him from going into the Low Country Wars, but could not prevail, his young Desires prompting him to run into the Army where he was kill'd; and tho' he said he would not cease to pray for me, yet he would venture to say to me, that if I did take this foolish Step, God would not bless me, and I would have Leisure hereafter to reflect upon having neglected his Counsel when there might be none to assiſt in my Recovery.

I observed in this laſt Part of his Discourse, which was truly Prophetick, tho' I suppose my Father did not know it to be so himself; I say, I observed the Tears run down his Face very plentifully, and especially when he spoke of my Brother who was kill'd; and that when he spoke of my

having Leisure to repent, and none to assist me, he was
so mov'd, that he broke off the Discourse, and told me,
his Heart was so full he could say no more to me.

I was sincerely affected with this Discourse, as indeed
who could be otherwise; and I resolv'd not to think of going abroad any more, but to settle at home according to
my Father's Desire. But alas! a few Days wore it all off;
and in short, to prevent any of my Father's farther Im-
portunities, in a few Weeks after, I resolv'd to run quite
away from him. However, I did not act so hastily neither
as my first Heat of Resolution prompted, but I took my
Mother, at a time when I thought her a little pleasanter
than ordinary, and told her, that my Thoughts were so
entirely bent upon seeing the World, that I should never
settle to any thing with Resolution enough to go through
with it, and my Father had better give me his Consent
than force me to go without it; that I was now Eighteen
Years old, which was too late to go Apprentice to a Trade,
or Clerk to an Attorney; that I was sure if I did, I should
never serve out my time, and I should certainly run away
from my Master before my Time was out, and go to Sea;
and if she would speak to my Father to let me go but one
Voyage abroad, if I came home again and did not like it, I
would go no more, and I would promise by a double Dili-
gence to recover that Time I had lost.

This put my Mother into a great Passion: She told
me, she knew it would be to no Purpose to speak to my
Father upon any such Subject; that he knew too well
what was my Interest to give his Consent to any thing so
much for my Hurt, and that she wondered how I could
think of any such thing after such a Discourse as I had
had with my Father, and such kind and tender Expres-
sions as she knew my Father had us'd to me; and that in

short, if I would ruine my self there was no Help for me; but I might depend I should never have their Consent to it: That for her Part she would not have so much Hand in my Destruction; and I should never have it to say, that my Mother was willing when my Father was not.

Tho' my Mother refused to move it to my Father, yet as I have heard afterwards, she reported all the Discourse to him, and that my Father, after shewing a great Concern at it, said to her with a Sigh, That Boy might be happy if he would stay at home, but if he goes abroad he will be the miserablest Wretch that was ever born: I can give no Consent to it.

It was not till almost a Year after this that I broke loose, tho' in the mean time I continued obstinately deaf to all Proposals of settling to Business, and frequently expostulating with my Father and Mother, about their being so positively determin'd against what they knew my Inclinations prompted me to. But being one Day at *Hull*, where I went casually, and without any Purpose of making an Elopement that time; but I say, being there, and one of my Companions being going by Sea to *London*, in his Father's Ship, and prompting me to go with them, with the common Allurement of Seafaring Men, *viz.* That it should cost me nothing for my Passage, I consulted neither Father or Mother any more, nor so much as sent them Word of it; but leaving them to hear of it as they might, without asking God's Blessing, or my Father's, without any Consideration of Circumstances or Consequences, and in an ill Hour, God knows, On the first of *September* 1651 I went on Board a Ship bound for *London*; never any young Adventurer's Misfortunes, I believe, began sooner, or continued longer than mine. The Ship was no sooner gotten out of the *Humber*, but the

Wind began to blow, and the Winds to rise in a most frightful manner; and as I had never been at Sea before, I was most inexpressibly sick in Body, and terrify'd in my Mind: I began now seriously to reflect upon what I had done, and how justly I was overtaken by the Judgment of Heaven for my wicked leaving my Father's House, and abandoning my Duty; all the good Counsel of my Parents, my Father's Tears and my Mother's Entreaties came now fresh into my Mind; and my Conscience, which was not yet come to the Pitch of Hardness to which it has been since, reproach'd me with the Contempt of Advice, and the Breach of my Duty to God and my Father.

All this while the Storm encreas'd, and the Sea, which I had never been upon before, went very high, tho' nothing like what I have seen many times since; no, nor like what I saw a few Days after: But it was enough to affect me then, who was but a young Sailor, and had never known any thing of the matter. I expected every Wave would have swallowed us up, and that every time the Ship fell down, as I thought, in the Trough or Hollow of the Sea, we should never rise more; and in this Agony of Mind, I made many Vows and Resolutions, that if it would please God here to spare my Life this one Voyage, if ever I got once my Foot upon dry Land again, I would go directly home to my Father, and never set it into a Ship again while I liv'd; that I would take his Advice, and never run my self into such Miseries as these any more. Now I saw plainly the Goodness of his Observations about the middle Station of Life, how easy, how comfortably he had liv'd all his Days, and never had been expos'd to Tempests at Sea, or Troubles on Shore; and I resolv'd that I would, like a true repenting Prodigal, go home to my Father.

These wise and sober Thoughts continued all the while the Storm continued, and indeed some time after; but the next Day the Wind was abated and the Sea calmer, and I began to be a little inur'd to it: However I was very grave for all that Day, being also a little Sea sick still; but towards Night the Weather clear'd up, the Wind was quite over, and a charming fine Evening follow'd; the Sun went down perfectly clear and rose so the next Morning; and having little or no Wind and a smooth Sea, the Sun shining upon it, the Sight was, as I thought, the most delightful that ever I saw.

I had slept well in the Night, and was now no more Sea sick but very chearful, looking with Wonder upon the Sea that was so rough and terrible the Day before, and could be so calm and so pleasant in so little time after. And now least my good Resolutions should continue, my Companion, who had indeed entic'd me away, comes to me, *Well* Bob, says he, clapping me on the Shoulder, *How do you do after it? I warrant you were frighted, wa'n't you, last Night, when it blew but a Cap full of Wind? A Cap full d'you call it?* said I, *'twas a terrible Storm*: *A Storm, you Fool you*, replies he, *do you call that a Storm, why it was nothing at all; give us but a good Ship and Sea Room, and we think nothing of such a Squall of Wind as that; but you're but a fresh Water Sailor*, Bob; *come let us make a Bowl of Punch and we'll forget all that, d'ye see what charming Weather 'tis now*. To make short this sad Part of my Story, we went the old way of all Sailors, the Punch was made, and I was made drunk with it, and in that one Night's Wickedness I drowned all my Repentance, all my Reflections upon my past Conduct, and all my Resolutions for my future. In a word, as the Sea was returned to its Smoothness of Surface and settled Calmness by the Abatement of that Storm, so the Hurry of my Thoughts being over, my Fears and Apprehensions of being swallow'd up by the Sea being forgotten, and the Current of my former Desires return'd, I entirely forgot the Vows and Promises that I made in my Distress. I found indeed some Intervals of Reflection, and the serious Thoughts did, as it were endeavour to return again sometimes, but I shook them off, and rouz'd my self from them as it were from a Distemper, and applying my self to Drink and Company, soon master'd the Return of those Fits, for so I call'd them, and I had in five or six Days got as compleat a Victory over Conscience as any young Fellow that resolv'd not to be troubled with it, could desire: But I was to have another Trial for it still; and Providence, as in such Cases generally it does, resolv'd to leave me entirely without Excuse. For if I would not take this for a Deliverance, the next was to be such a one as the worst and most harden'd Wretch among us would confess both the Danger and the Mercy.

The sixth Day of our being at Sea we came into *Yarmouth* Roads; the Wind having been contrary, and the Weather calm, we had made but little Way since the Storm. Here we were obliged to come to an Anchor, and here we lay, the Wind continuing contrary, *viz.* at Southwest, for seven or eight Days, during which time a great many Ships from *Newcastle* came into the same Roads, as the common Harbour where the Ships might wait for a Wind for the River.

We had not however rid here so long, but should have Tided it up the River, but that the Wind blew too fresh; and after we had lain four or five Days, blew very hard. However, the Roads being reckoned as good as a Harbour, the Anchorage good, and our Ground-Tackle very strong, our Men were unconcerned, and not in the least apprehensive of Danger, but spent the Time in Rest and Mirth, after the manner of the Sea; but the eighth Day in the Morning, the Wind increased, and we had all Hands at Work to strike our Top-Masts, and make every thing snug and close, that the Ship might ride as easy as possible. By Noon the Sea went very high indeed, and our Ship rid *Forecastle in*, shipp'd several Seas, and we thought once or twice our Anchor had come home; upon which our Master order'd out the Sheet Anchor; so that we rode with two Anchors a-Head, and the Cables vered out to the better End.

By this Time it blew a terrible Storm indeed, and now I began to see Terror and Amazement in the Faces even of the Seamen themselves. The Master, tho' vigilant to the Business of preserving the Ship, yet as he went in and out of his Cabbin by me, I could hear him softly to himself say several times, *Lord be merciful to us, we shall be all lost, we shall be all undone*; and the like. During these first Hurries, I was stupid, lying still in my Cabbin, which was in the Steerage, and cannot describe my Temper: I could ill re-assume the first Penitence, which I had so apparently trampled upon, and harden'd my self against: I thought the Bitterness of Death had been past, and that this would be nothing too like the first. But when the Master himself came by me, as I said just now, and said we should be all lost, I was dreadfully frighted: I got up out of my Cabbin, and look'd out; but such a dismal Sight I never saw: The Sea went Mountains high, and broke upon us every three or four Minutes: when I could look about, I could see nothing but Distress round us: Two Ships that rid near us we found had cut their Masts by the Board, being deep loaden; and our Men cry'd out,

R. Crusoe Shipwreckt at Yarmouth

to lie near the Ship Side, till at laſt the Men rowing very heartily, and venturing their Lives to save ours, our Men caſt them a Rope over the Stern with a Buoy to it, and then vered it out a great Length, which they after great Labour and Hazard took hold of, and we hawl'd them close under our Stern and got all into their Boat. It was to no Purpose for them or us after we were in the Boat to think of reaching to their own Ship, so all agreed to let her drive and only to pull her in towards Shore as much as we could, and our Maſter promised them, That if the Boat was ſtav'd upon Shore he would make it good to their Maſter, so partly rowing and partly driving, our Boat went away to the Norward sloaping towards the Shore almoſt as far as *Winterton Ness.*

We were not much more than a quarter of an Hour out of our Ship but we saw her sink, and then I under-ſtood for the firſt time what was meant by a Ship founder-ing in the Sea; I muſt acknowledge I had hardly Eyes to look up when the Seamen told me she was sinking; for from that Moment they rather put me into the Boat than that I might be said to go in, my Heart was as it were dead within me, partly with Fright, partly with Horror of Mind and the Thoughts of what was yet before me.

While we were in this Condition, the Men yet labour-ing at the Oar to bring the Boat near the Shore, we could see, when our Boat mounting the Waves, we were able to see the Shore, a great many People running along the Shore to assiſt us when we should come near, but we made but slow way towards the Shore, nor were we able to reach the Shore, till being paſt the Light-House at *Winterton,* the Shore falls off to the Weſtward towards *Cromer,* and so the Land broke off a little the Violence of the Wind: Here we got in, and tho' not without much Difficulty got all safe on Shore, and walk'd afterwards on Foot to *Yar-mouth*, where, as unfortunate Men, we were used with great Humanity as well by the Magistrates of the Town, who assign'd us good Quarters, as by particular Merchants and Owners of Ships, and had Money given us sufficient to carry us either to *London* or back to Hull, as we thought fit.

Had I now had the Sense to have gone back to *Hull*, and have gone home, I had been happy, and my Father, an Emblem of our Blessed Saviour's Parable, had even kill'd the fatted Calf for me; for hearing the Ship I went away in was cast away in *Yarmouth* Road, it was a great while before he had any Assurance that I was not drown'd.

But my ill Fate push'd me on now with an Obstinacy that nothing could resist; and tho' I had several times loud Calls from my Reason and my more composed Judgment to go home, yet I had no Power to do it. I know not what to call this, nor will I urge, that it is a secret over-ruling Decree that hurries us on to be the Instruments of our own Destruction, even tho' it be before us, and that we rush upon it with our Eyes open. Certainly nothing but some such decreed unavoidable Misery attending, and which it was impossible for me to escape, could have push'd me forward against the calm Reasonings and Perswasions of my most retired Thoughts, and against two such visible Instructions as I had met with in my first Attempt.

My Comrade, who had help'd to harden me before, and who was the Master's Son, was now less forward than I; the first time he spoke to me after we were at *Yarmouth*, which was not till two or three Days, for we were separated in the Town to several Quarters; I say, the first time he saw me, it appear'd his Tone was alter'd, and looking very melancholy and shaking his Head, ask'd me how I did, and telling his Father who I was, and how I had come this Voyage only for a Trial in order to go farther abroad; his Father turning to me with a very grave and concern'd Tone, *Young Man*, says he, *you ought never to go to Sea any more, you ought to take this for a plain and visible Token that you are not to be a Seafaring Man.* Why, Sir, said I, will you go to Sea no more? *That is another Case*, said he, *it is my Calling, and therefore my Duty; but as you made this Voyage for a Trial, you see what a Taste Heaven has given you of what you are to expect if you persist; perhaps this is all befallen us on your Account, like* Jonah *in the Ship of* Tarshish. *Pray*, continues he, *what are you? and on what Account did you go to Sea?* Upon that I told him some of my Story; at the End of which he burst out with a strange kind of Passion, What had I done, says he, that such an unhappy Wretch should come into my Ship? I would not set my Foot in the same Ship with thee again for a Thousand Pounds. This indeed was, as I said, an Excursion of his Spirits which were yet agitated by the Sense of his Loss, and was farther than he could have Authority to go. However he afterwards talk'd very gravely to me, exhorted me to go back to my Father, and not tempt Providence to my Ruine; told me I might see a visible Hand of Heaven against me, *And young Man*, said he, *depend upon it, if you do not go back, where-ever you go, you will meet with nothing but Disasters and Disappointments till your Father's Words are fulfilled upon you.*

We parted soon after; for I made him little Answer, and I saw him no more; which way he went, I know not. As for me, having some Money in my Pocket, I travelled to *London* by Land; and there, as well as on the Road, had many Struggles with my self, what Course of Life I should take, and whether I should go Home, or go to Sea.

As to going Home, Shame opposed the best Motions that offered to my Thoughts; and it immediately oc-curr'd to me how I should be laugh'd at among the Neigh-bours, and should be asham'd to see, not my Father and Mother only, but even every Body else; from whence I have since often observed, how incongruous and irra-tional the common Temper of Mankind is, especially of Youth, to that Reason which ought to guide them in such Cases, *viz.* That they are not asham'd to sin, and yet are asham'd to repent; not asham'd of the Action for which they ought justly to be esteemed Fools, but are asham'd of the returning, which only can make them be esteem'd wise Men.

In this State of Life however I remained some time, un-certain what Measures to take, and what Course of Life to lead. An irresistible Reluctance continu'd to going Home; and as I stay'd a while, the Remembrance of the Distress I had been in wore off; and as that abated, the little Motion I had in my Desires to a Return wore off with it, till at last I quite lay'd aside the Thoughts of it, and lookt out for a Voyage.

That evil Influence which carryed me first away from my Father's House, that hurried me into the wild and in-digested Notion of raising my Fortune; and that imprest those Conceits so forcibly upon me, as to make me deaf to all good Advice, and to the Entreaties and even Com-mand of my Father: I say the same Influence, whatever it was, presented the most unfortunate of all Enterprises to my View; and I went on board a Vessel bound to the Coast of *Africa*; or, as our Sailors vulgarly call it, a Voyage to *Guinea*.

It was my great Misfortune that in all these Adventures I did not ship my self as a Sailor; whereby, tho' I might indeed have workt a little harder than ordinary, yet at the same time I had learn'd the Duty and Office of a Fore-maſt Man; and in time might have quallified my self for a Mate or Lieutenant, if not for a Maſter: But as it was always my Fate to choose for the worse, so I did here; for having Money in my Pocket, and good Cloaths upon my Back, I would always go on board in the Habit of a Gentleman; and so I neither had any Business in the Ship, or learn'd to do any.

It was my Lot firſt of all to fall into pretty good Company in *London*, which does not always happen to such loose and unguided young Fellows as I then was; the Devil generally not omitting to lay some Snare for them very early: But it was not so with me, I firſt fell acquainted with the Maſter of a Ship who had been on the Coaſt of *Guinea*; and who having had very good Success there, was resolved to go again; and who taking a Fancy to my Conversation, which was not at all disagreeable at that time, hearing me say I had a mind to see the World, told me if I wou'd go the Voyage with him I should be at no Expence; I should be his Mess-mate and his Companion, and if I could carry any thing with me, I should have all the Advantage of it that the Trade would admit; and perhaps I might meet with some Encouragement.

I embrac'd the Offer, and entring into a ſtriƈt Friendship with this Captain, who was an honeſt and plain-dealing Man, I went the Voyage with him, and carried a small Adventure with me, which by the disintereſted Honeſty of my Friend the Captain, I increased very considerably; for I carried about 40 *l.* in such Toys and Trifles as the Captain direƈted me to buy. This 40 *l.* I had muſtered together by the Assistance of some of my Relations whom I corresponded with, and who, I believe, got my Father, or at least my Mother, to contribute so much as that to my first Adventure.

This was the only Voyage which I may say was successful in all my Adventures, and which I owe to the Integrity and Honesty of my Friend the Captain, under whom also I got a competent Knowledge of the Mathematicks and the Rules of Navigation, learn'd how to keep an Account of the Ship's Course, take an Observation; and in short, to understand some things that were needful to be understood by a Sailor: For, as he took Delight to introduce me, I took Delight to learn; and, in a word, this Voyage made me both a Sailor and a Merchant: for I brought home *L. 5. 9 Ounces* of Gold Dust for my Adventure, which yielded me in *London* at my Return, almost 300 *l.* and this fill'd me with those aspiring Thoughts which have since so compleated my Ruin.

Yet even in this Voyage I had my Misfortunes too; particularly, that I was continually sick, being thrown into a violent Calenture by the excessive Heat of the Climate; our principal Trading being upon the Coast, from the Latitude of 15 Degrees, North even to the Line it self.

I was now set up for a *Guiney* Trader; and my Friend, to my great Misfortune, dying soon after his Arrival, I resolved to go the same Voyage again, and I embark'd in the same Vessel with one who was his Mate in the former Voyage, and had now got the Command of the Ship. This was the unhappiest Voyage that ever Man made; for tho' I did not carry quite 100 *l.* of my new gain'd Wealth, so that I had 200 left, and which I lodg'd with my Friend's Widow, who was very just to me, yet I fell

into terrible Misfortunes in this Voyage; and the firſt
was this, *viz.* Our Ship making her Course towards the
Canary Islands, or rather between those Islands and the
African Shore, was surprised in the Grey of the Morning,
by a *Turkish* Rover of *Sallee*, who gave Chase to us with
all the Sail she could make. We crowded also as much
Canvass as our Yards would spread, or our Maſts carry,
to have got clear; but finding the Pirate gain'd upon us,
and would certainly come up with us in a few Hours, we
prepar'd to fight; our Ship having 12 Guns, and the Ro-
gue 18. About three in the Afternoon he came up with
us, and bringing to by Miſtake, juſt athwart our Quarter, inſtead of athwart our Stern, as he intended, we
brought 8 of our Guns to bear on that Side, and pour'd
in a Broadside upon him, which made him sheer off again,
after returning our Fire, and pouring in also his small
Shot from near 200 Men which he had on Board. However, we had not a Man touch'd, all our Men keeping
close. He prepar'd to attack us again, and we to defend
our selves; but laying us on Board the next time upon our
other Quarter, he entred 60 Men upon our Decks, who
immediately fell to cutting and hacking the Decks and
Rigging. We ply'd them with Small-shot, Half-Pikes,
Powder-Cheſts, and such like, and clear'd our Deck of
them twice. However, to cut short this melancholly Part
of our Story, our Ship being disabled, and three of our
Men kill'd, and eight wounded, we were obliged to yield,
and were carry'd all Prisoners into *Sallee*, a Port belonging to the *Moors*.

The Usage I had there was not so dreadful as at firſt I
apprehended, nor was I carried up the Country to the
Emperor's Court, as the reſt of our Men were, but was
kept by the Captain of the Rover, as his proper Prize, and

made his Slave, being young and nimble, and fit for his
Business. At this surprising Change of my Circumstances
from a Merchant to a miserable Slave, I was perfectly
overwhelmed; and now I look'd back upon my Father's
prophetick Discourse to me, that I should be miserable,
and have none to relieve me, which I thought was now so
effectually brought to pass, that it could not be worse;
that now the Hand of Heaven had overtaken me, and I
was undone without Redemption. But alas! this was but
a Taste of the Misery I was to go thro', as will appear in
the Sequel of this Story.

As my new Patron or Master had taken me Home to
his House, so I was in hopes that he would take me with
him when he went to Sea again, believing that it would
some time or other be his Fate to be taken by a *Spanish* or
Portugal Man of War; and that then I should be set at
Liberty. But this Hope of mine was soon taken away; for
when he went to Sea, he left me on Shoar to look after his
little Garden, and do the common Drudgery of Slaves
about his House; and when he came home again from
his Cruise, he order'd me to lye in the Cabbin to look after
the Ship.

Here I meditated nothing but my Escape; and what
Method I might take to effect it, but found no Way that
had the least Probability in it: Nothing presented to make
the Supposition of it rational; for I had no Body to com-
municate it to, that would embark with me; no Fellow-
Slave, no *Englishman, Irishman,* or *Scotsman* there but my
self; so that for two Years, tho' I often pleased my self
with the Imagination, yet I never had the least encouraging Prospect of putting it in Practice.

After about two Years an odd Circumstance presented it self, which put the old Thought of making some

Attempt for my Liberty, again in my Head: My Patron lying at Home longer than usual, without fitting out his Ship, which, as I heard, was for want of Money; he used constantly, once or twice a Week, sometimes oftner, if the Weather was fair, to take the Ship's Pinnace, and go out into the Road a-fishing; and as he always took me and a young *Maresco* with him to row the Boat, we made him very merry, and I prov'd very dexterous in catching Fish; insomuch that sometimes he would send me with a *Moor*, one of his Kinsmen, and the Youth the *Maresco*, as they call'd him, to catch a Dish of Fish for him.

It happen'd one time, that going a fishing in a stark calm Morning, a Fog rose so thick, that tho' we were not half a League from the Shoar, we lost Sight of it; and rowing we knew not whither or which way, we labour'd all Day and all the next Night, and when the Morning came we found we had pull'd off to Sea instead of pulling in for the Shoar; and that we were at least two Leagues from the Shoar: However we got well in again, tho' with a great deal of Labour, and some Danger; for the Wind began to blow pretty fresh in the Morning; but particularly we were all very hungry.

But our Patron warn'd by this Disaster, resolved to take more Care of himself for the future; and having lying by him the Long-boat of our *English* Ship they had taken, he resolved he would not go a fishing any more without a Compass and some Provision; so he ordered the Carpenter of his Ship, who also was an *English* Slave, to build a little State-room or Cabin in the middle of the Long Boat, like that of a Barge, with a Place to stand behind it to steer and hale home the Main-sheet; and Room before for a hand or two to stand and work the Sails; she sail'd with that we call a Shoulder of Mutton Sail; and the

Boom gib'd over the Top of the Cabbin, which lay very snug and low, and had in it Room for him to lye, with a Slave or two, and a Table to eat on, with some small Lockers to put in some Bottles of such Liquor as he thought fit to drink; particularly his Bread, Rice and Coffee.

We went frequently out with this Boat a fishing, and as I was moſt dextrous to catch fish for him, he never went without me: It happen'd that he had appointed to go out in this Boat, either for Pleasure or for Fish, with two or three *Moors* of some Diſtinction in that Place, and for whom he had provided extraordinarily; and had therefore sent on board the Boat over Night, a larger Store of Provisions than ordinary; and had order'd me to get ready three Fuzees with Powder and Shot, which were on board his Ship; for that they design'd some Sport of Fowling as well as Fishing.

I got all things ready as he had directed, and waited the next Morning with the Boat, washed clean, her Antient and Pendants out, and every thing to accomodate his Gueſts; when by and by my Patroon came on board alone, and told me his Gueſts had put off going, upon some Business that fell out, and order'd me with the Man and Boy, as usual, to go out with the Boat and catch them some Fish, for that his Friends were to sup at his House; and commanded that as soon as I had got some Fish I should bring it home to his House; all which I prepar'd to do.

This Moment my former Notions of Deliverance darted into my Thoughts, for now I found I was like to have a little Ship at my Command; and my Maſter being gone, I prepar'd to furnish my self, not for a fishing Business but for a Voyage; tho' I knew not, neither did I so much as consider whither I should ſteer; for any where to get out of that Place was my Way.

My firſt Contrivance was to make a Pretence to speak to this *Moor*, to get something for our Subsiſtance on board; for I told him we muſt not presume to eat of our Patroon's Bread; he said, that was true; so he brought a large Basket of Rusk or Bisket of their kind, and three Jarrs with fresh Water into the Boat; I knew where my Patroon's Case of Bottles ſtood, which it was evident by the make were taken out of some *English* Prize; and I convey'd them into the Boat while the *Moor* was on Shoar, as if they had been there before, for our Maſter: I convey'd also a great Lump of Bees-Wax into the Boat, which weighed above half a Hundred Weight, with a Parcel of Twine or Thread, a Hatchet, a Saw and a Hammer, all which were of great Use to us afterwards; especially the Wax to make Candles. Another Trick I try'd upon him, which he innocently came into also; his Name was *Ismael*, who they call *Muly* or *Moely*, so I call'd to him, *Moely* said I, our Patroon's Guns are on board the Boat, can you not get a little Powder and Shot, it may be we may kill some *Alcamies* (a Fowl like our *Curlieus*) for our selves, for I know he keeps the Gunner's Stores in the Ship? Yes, *says he*, I'll bring some, and accordingly he brought a great Leather Pouch which held about a Pound and half of Powder, or rather more; and another with Shot, that had five or six Pound, with some Bullets; and put all into the Boat: At the same time I had found some Powder of my Maſter's in the Great Cabbin, with which I fill'd one of the large Bottles in the Case, which was almoſt empty; pouring what was in it into another: and thus furnished with every thing needful, we sail'd out of the Port to fish: The Caſtle which is at the Entrance of the Port knew who we were, and took no Notice of us; and we were not above a Mile out of the Port before we hal'd in our Sail, and set us down to fish: The Wind blew from the N.NE. which was contrary to my Desire; for had it blown southerly I had been sure to have made the Coast of *Spain*, and at least reacht to the Bay of *Cadiz*; but my Resolutions were, blow which way it would, I would be gone from that horrid Place where I was, and leave the rest to Fate.

After we had fisht some time and catcht nothing, for when I had Fish on my Hook, I would not pull them up, that he might not see them; I said to the *Moor*, this will not do, our Master will not be thus serv'd, we must stand farther off: He thinking no harm agreed, and being in the Head of the Boat set the Sails; and as I had the Helm I run the Boat out near a League farther, and then brought her too as if I would fish; when giving the Boy the Helm, I stept forward to where the *Moor* was, and making as if I stoopt for something behind him, I took him by Surprize with my Arm under his Twist, and tost him clear over-board into the Sea; he rise immediately, for he swam like a Cork, and call'd to me, begg'd to be taken in, told me he would go all over the World with me; he swam so strong after the Boat that he would have reacht me very quickly, there being but little Wind; upon which I stept into the Cabbin and fetching one of the Fowling-pieces, I presented it at him, and told him, I had done him no hurt, and if he would be quiet I would do him none; but said I, you swim well enough to reach to the Shoar, and the Sea is calm, make the best of your Way to Shoar and I will do you no harm, but if you come near the Boat I'll shoot you thro' the Head; for I am resolved to have my Liberty; so he turn'd himself about and swam for the

Shoar, and I make no doubt but he reacht it with Ease, for he was an Excellent Swimmer.

I could ha' been content to ha' taken this *Moor* with me, and ha' drown'd the Boy, but there was no venturing to truſt him: When he was gone I turn'd to the Boy, who they call'd *Xury*, and said to him, *Xury*, if you will be faithful to me I'll make you a great Man, but if you will not ſtroak your Face to be true to me, *that is, swear by* Mahomet *and his Father's Beard*, I muſt throw you into the Sea too; the Boy smil'd in my Face and spoke so innocently that I could not miſtruſt him; and swore to be faithful to me, and go all over the World with me.

While I was in View of the *Moor* that was swimming, I ſtood out directly to Sea with the Boat, rather ſtretching to Windward, that they might think me gone towards the *Straits*-mouth (as indeed any one that had been in their Wits muſt ha' been supposed to do) for who would ha' suppos'd we were saild on to the southward to the truly *Barbarian* Coaſt, where whole Nations of Negroes were sure to surround us with their Canoes, and deſtroy us; where we could ne'er once go on shoar but we should be devour'd by savage Beaſts, or more merciless Savages of humane kind.

But as soon as it grew dusk in the Evening, I chang'd my Course, and ſteer'd directly South and by Eaſt, bending my Course a little toward the Eaſt, that I might keep in with the Shoar; and having a fair fresh Gale of Wind, and a smooth quiet Sea, I made such Sail that I believe by the next Day at Three a Clock in the Afternoon, when I firſt made the Land, I could not be less than 1 50 Miles South of *Sallee*; quite beyond the Emperor of *Morocco's* Dominions, or indeed of any other King thereabouts, for we saw no People.

Yet such was the Fright I had taken at the *Moors*, and the dreadful Apprehensions I had of falling into their Hands, that I would not ſtop, or go on Shoar, or come to an Anchor; the Wind continuing fair, 'till I had sail'd in that manner five Days: And then the Wind shifting to the southward, I concluded also that if any of our Vessels were in Chase of me, they also would now give over; so I ventur'd to make to the Coaſt, and came to an Anchor in the Mouth of a little River, I knew not what, or where; neither what Latitude, what Country, what Nations, or what River: I neither saw, or desir'd to see any People, the principal thing I wanted was fresh Water: We came into this Creek in the Evening, resolving to swim on shoar as soon as it was dark, and discover the Country; but as soon as it was quite dark, we heard such dreadful Noises of the Barking, Roaring, and Howling of Wild Creatures, of we knew not what Kinds, that the poor Boy was ready to die with Fear, and beg'd of me not to go on shoar till Day; well *Xury* said I, then I won't, but it may be we may see Men by Day, who will be as bad to us as those Lyons; *then we give them the shoot Gun* says *Xury* laughing, *make them run wey*; such *English Xury* spoke by conversing among us Slaves, however I was glad to see the Boy so cheerful, and I gave him a Dram (out of our Patroon's Case of Bottles) to chear him up: After all, *Xury*'s Advice was good, and I took it, we dropt our little Anchor and lay ſtill all Night; I say ſtill, for we slept none! for in two or three Hours we saw vaſt great Creatures (we knew not what to call them) of many sorts, come down to the Sea-shoar and run into the Water, wallowing and washing themselves for the Pleasure of cooling themselves; and they made such hideous Howlings and Yellings, that I never indeed heard the like.

Xury was dreadfully frighted, and indeed so was I too; but we were both more frighted when we heard one of these mighty Creatures come swimming towards our Boat, we could not see him, but we might hear him by his blowing to be a monstrous, huge and furious Beast; *Xury* said it was a Lyon, and it might be so for ought I know; but poor *Xury* cryed to me to weigh the Anchor and row away; no says I, *Xury*, we can slip our Cable with the Buoy to it and go off to Sea, they cannot follow us far; I had no sooner said so, but I perceiv'd the Creature (whatever it was) within Two Oars Length, which something surprized me; however I immediately stept to the Cabbin-door, and taking up my Gun fir'd at him, upon which he immediately turn'd about and swam towards the Shoar again.

But it is impossible to describe the horrible Noises, and hideous Cryes and Howlings, that were raised as well upon the Edge of the Shoar, as higher within the Country; upon the Noise or Report of the Gun, a Thing I have some Reason to believe those Creatures had never heard before: This Convinc'd me that there was no going on Shoar for us in the Night upon that Coast, and how to venture on Shoar in the Day was another Question too; for to have fallen into the Hands of any of the Savages, had been as bad as to have fallen into the Hands of Lyons and Tygers; at least we were equally apprehensive of the Danger of it.

Be that as it would, we were oblig'd to go on Shoar somewhere or other for Water, for we had not a Pint left in the Boat; when or where to get to it was the Point: *Xury* said, if I would let him go on Shoar with one of the Jarrs, he would find if there was any Water and bring some to me. I ask'd him why he would go? why I should not go and he ſtay in the Boat? The Boy answer'd with so much Affeċtion that made me love him ever after. Says he, *If wild Mans come, they eat me, you go wey.* Well, *Xury,* said I, we will both go, and if the wild Man's come we will kill them, they shall Eat neither of us; so I gave *Xury* a piece of Rusk-bread to Eat and a Dram out of our Patroon's Case of Bottles which I mentioned before; and we hal'd the Boat in as near the Shoar as we thought was proper, and so waded on Shoar, carrying nothing but our Arms and two Jarrs for Water.

I did not care to go out of Sight of the Boat, fearing the coming of Canoes with *Savages* down the River; but the Boy seeing a low Place about a Mile up the Country rambled to it; and by and by I saw him come running towards me, I thought he was pursued by some Savage, or frighted with some wild Beaſt, and I run forward towards him to help him, but when I came nearer to him, I saw something hanging over his Shoulders which was a Creature that he had shot, like a Hare but different in Colour, and longer Legs, however we were very glad of it, and it was very good Meat; but the great Joy that poor *Xury* came with, was to tell me he had found good Water and seen no wild Mans.

But we found afterwards that we need not take such Pains for Water, for a little higher up the Creek where we were, we found the Water fresh when the Tide was out, which flowed but a little way up; so we filled our Jarrs and feaſted on the Hare we had killed, and prepared to go on our Way, having seen no Foot-ſteps of any humane Creature in that part of the Country.

As I had been one Voyage to this Coaſt before, I knew very well that the Islands of the *Canaries,* and the *Cape de Verd* Islands also, lay not far off from the Coaſt. But as I had no Inſtruments to take an Observation to know what Latitude we were in, and did not exaƈtly know, or at leaſt remember what Latitude they were in; I knew not where to look for them, or when to ſtand off to Sea towards them; otherwise I might now easily have found some of these Islands. But my hope was, that if I ſtood along this Coaſt till I came to that Part where the *English* Traded, I should find some of their Vessels upon their usual Design of Trade, that would relieve and take us in.

By the beſt of my Calculation, that Place where I now was, muſt be that Country, which lying between the Emperor of *Morocco*'s Dominions and the *Negro*'s, lies waſt and uninhabited, except by wild Beaſts; the *Negroes* having abandon'd it and gone farther South for fear of the *Moors*; and the *Moors* not thinking it worth inhabiting, by reason of its Barrenness; and indeed both forsaking it because of the prodigious Numbers of Tygers, Lyons, Leopards and other furious Creatures which harbour there; so that the *Moors* use it for their Hunting only, where they go like an Army, two or three thousand Men at a time; and indeed for near an hundred Miles together upon this Coaſt, we saw nothing but a waſt uninhabited Country, by Day; and heard nothing but Howlings and Roaring of wild Beaſts, by Night.

Once or twice in the Day time, I thought I saw the *Pico* of *Teneriffe*, being the high top of the Mountain *Teneriffe* in the *Canaries*; and had a great mind to venture out in hopes of reaching thither; but having tried twice I was forced in again by contrary Winds, the Sea also going too high for my little Vessel, so I resolved to pursue my firſt Design and keep along the Shoar.

Several times I was obliged to land for fresh Water, after we had left this Place; and once in particular, being

early in the Morning, we came to an Anchor under a little
Point of Land which was pretty high, and the Tide beginning to flow, we lay ſtill to go farther in; *Xury*, whose
Eyes were more about him than it seems mine were, calls
softly to me, and tells me that we had beſt go farther off
the Shoar; for, says he, look yonder lies a dreadful Monſter on the side of that Hillock faſt asleep: I look'd where
he pointed, and saw a dreadful Monſter indeed, for it was
a terrible great Lyon that lay on the Side of the Shoar, under the Shade of a Piece of the Hill that hung as it were
a little over him. *Xury*, says I, you shall go on Shoar and
kill him; *Xury* look'd frighted, and said, *Me kill! he eat
me at one Mouth*; one Mouthful he meant; however, I
said no more to the Boy, but bad him lye ſtill, and I took
our biggeſt Gun, which was almoſt Musquet-bore, and
loaded it with a good Charge of Powder, and with two
Slugs, and laid it down; then I loaded another Gun with
two Bullets, and the third, for we had three Pieces, I
loaded with five smaller Bullets. I took the beſt aim I
could with the firſt Piece to have shot him into the Head,
but he lay so with his Leg rais'd a little above his Nose,
that the Slugs hit his Leg about the Knee, and broke the
Bone. He ſtarted up growling at firſt, but finding his
Leg broke fell down again, and then got up upon three
Legs and gave the moſt hideous Roar that ever I heard;
I was a little surpriz'd that I had not hit him on the Head;
however I took up the second Piece immediately, and
tho' he began to move off fir'd again, and shot him into
the Head, and had the Pleasure to see him drop, and
make but little Noiſe, but lay ſtruggling for Life. Then
Xury took Heart, and would have me let him go on
Shoar: Well, go said I; so the Boy jump'd into the Water,
and taking a little Gun in one Hand swam to Shoar with

the other Hand, and coming close to the Creature, put the Muzzle of the Piece to his Ear, and shot him into the Head again which dispatch'd him quite.

This was Game indeed to us, but this was no Food, and I was very sorry to lose three Charges of Powder and Shot upon a Creature that was good for nothing to us. However *Xury* said he would have some of him; so he comes on board, and ask'd me to give him the Hatchet; for what, *Xury*, said I? *Me cut off his Head*, said he. However *Xury* could not cut off his Head, but he cut off a Foot and brought it with him, and it was a monstrous great one.

I bethought my self however, that perhaps the Skin of him might one way or other be of some Value to us; and I resolved to take off his Skin if I could. So *Xury* and I went to work with him; but *Xury* was much the better Workman at it, for I knew very ill how to do it. Indeed it took us up both the whole Day, but at last we got off the Hide of him, and spreading it on the top of our Cabbin, the Sun effectually dried it in two Days time, and it afterwards serv'd me to lye upon.

After this Stop we made on to the Southward continually for ten or twelve Days, living very sparing on our Provisions, which began to abate very much, and going no oftner into the Shoar than we were oblig'd to for fresh Water; my Design in this was to make the River *Gambia* or *Senegall*, that is to say, any where about the *Cape de Verd*, where I was in hopes to meet with some *European* Ship, and if I did not, I knew not what Course I had to take, but to seek out for the *Islands*, or perish there among the *Negroes*. I knew that all the Ships from *Europe*, which sail'd either to the Coast of *Guiney*, or to *Brasil*, or to the *East-Indies*, made this *Cape* or those *Islands*; and in a word, I put the whole of my Fortune upon this single

Point, either that I muſt meet with some Ship, or muſt perish.

When I had pursued this Resolution about ten Days longer, as I have said, I began to see that the Land was inhabited, and in two or three Places as we sailed by, we saw People ſtand upon the Shoar to look at us, we could also perceive they were quite Black and Stark-naked. I was once inclin'd to ha' gone on Shoar to them; but *Xury* was my better Councellor, and said to me, *no go, no go*; however I hal'd in nearer the Shoar that I might talk to them, and I found they run along the Shoar by me a good way; I observ'd they had no Weapons in their Hands, except one who had a long slender Stick, which *Xury* said was a Lance, and that they would throw them a great way with good aim; so I kept at a diſtance, but talk'd with them by Signs as well as I could; and particularly made Signs for some thing to Eat, they beckon'd to me to ſtop my Boat, and that they would fetch me some Meat; upon this I lower'd the top of my Sail, and lay by, and two of them run up into the Country, and in less than half an Hour came back and brought with them two Pieces of dry Flesh and some Corn, such as is the Produce of their Country, but we neither knew what the one or the other was; however we were willing to accept it, but how to come at it was our next Dispute, for I was not for venturing on Shore to them, and they were as much afraid of us; but they took a safe way for us all, for they brought it to the Shore and laid it down, and went and ſtood a great way off till we fetch'd it on Board, and then came close to us again.

We made Signs of Thanks to them, for we had nothing to make them amends; but an Opportunity offer'd that very Inſtant to oblige them wonderfully, for while

R.Crusoe and his boy Xury on the Coast of Guinny shooting a Lyon

we were lying by the Shore, came two mighty Creatures one pursuing the other, (as we took it) with great Fury, from the Mountains towards the Sea; whether it was the Male pursuing the Female, or whether they were in Sport or in Rage, we could not tell, any more than we could tell whether it was usual or ſtrange, but I believe it was the latter; because in the firſt Place, those ravenous Creatures seldom appear but in the Night; and in the second Place, we found the People terribly frighted, especially the Women. The Man that had the Lance or Dart did not fly from them, but the reſt did; however as the two Creatures ran direĉtly into the Water, they did not seem to offer to fall upon any of the *Negroes*, but plung'd themselves into the Sea and swam about as if they had come for their Diversion; at laſt one of them began to come nearer our Boat than at firſt I expeĉted, but I lay ready for him, for I had loaded my Gun with all possible Expedition, and bad *Xury* load both the other; as soon as he came fairly within my reach, I fir'd, and shot him direĉtly into the Head; immediately he sunk down into the Water, but rose inſtantly and plung'd up and down as if he was ſtruggling for Life; and so indeed he was, he immediately made to the Shore, but between the Wound which was his mortal Hurt, and the ſtrangling of the Water, he dyed juſt before he reach'd the Shore.

It is impossible to express the Aſtonishment of these poor Creatures at the Noise and the Fire of my Gun; some of them were even ready to dye for Fear, and fell down as Dead with the very Terror. But when they saw the Creature dead and sunk in the Water, and that I made Signs to them to come to the Shore; they took Heart and came to the Shore and began to search for the Creature, I found him by his Blood ſtaining the Water, and by the help of a Rope which I slung round him and gave the *Negroes* to hawl, they drag'd him on Shore, and found that it was a most curious Leopard, spotted and fine to an admirable Degree, and the *Negroes* held up their Hands with Admiration to think what it was I had kill'd him with.

The other Creature frighted with the flash of Fire and the Noise of the Gun swam on Shore, and ran up directly to the Mountains from whence they came, nor could I at that Distance know what it was. I found quickly the *Negroes* were for eating the Flesh of this Creature, so I was willing to have them take it as a Favour from me, which when I made Signs to them that they might take him, they were very thankful for, immediately they fell to work with him, and tho' they had no Knife, yet with a sharpen'd Piece of Wood they took off his Skin as readily and much more readily than we cou'd have done with a Knife; they offer'd me some of the Flesh, which I declined, making as if I would give it them, but made Signs for the Skin, which they gave me very freely, and brought me a great deal more of their Provision, which tho' I did not understand, yet I accepted; then I made Signs to them for some Water, and held out one of my Jarrs to them, turning it bottom upward, to shew that it was empty, and that I wanted to have it filled. They call'd immediately to some of their Friends, and there came two Women and brought a great Vessel made of Earth, and burnt as I suppose in the Sun; this they set down for me, as before, and I sent *Xury* on Shore with my Jarrs, and filled them all three: The Women were as stark Naked as the Men.

I was now furnished with Roots and Corn, such as it was, and Water, and leaving my friendly *Negroes*, I made

forward for about eleven Days more without offering to
go near the Shoar, till I saw the Land run out a great
Length into the Sea, at about the Diſtance of four or five
Leagues before me, and the Sea being very calm I kept a
large offing to make this Point; at length, doubling the
Point at about two Leagues from the Land, I saw plainly
Land on the other Side to Seaward; then I concluded, as
it was moſt certain indeed, that this was the *Cape de Verd*,
and those the *Islands*, call'd from thence *Cape de Verd Islands*. However they were at a great Diſtance, and I could
not well tell what I had beſt to do, for if I should be taken
with a Fresh of Wind I might neither reach one or other.

In this Dilemna, as I was very pensive, I ſtept into the
Cabbin and sat me down, *Xury* having the Helm, when
on a suddain the Boy cry'd out, *Maſter, Maſter, a Ship with
a Sail*, and the foolish Boy was frighted out of his Wits,
thinking it muſt needs be some of his Maſter's Ships
sent to pursue us, when, I knew we were gotten far
enough out of their reach. I jump'd out of the Cabbin,
and immediately saw not only the Ship, but what she was,
(*viz.*) that it was a *Portuguese* Ship, and as I thought was
bound to the Coaſt of *Guinea* for *Negroes*. But when I observ'd the Course she ſteer'd, I was soon convinc'd they
were bound some other way, and did not design to come
any nearer to the Shoar; upon which I ſtretch'd out to
Sea as much as I could, resolving to speak with them if
possible.

With all the Sail I could make, I found I should not be
able to come in their Way, but that they would be gone
by, before I could make any Signal to them; but after I
had crowded to the utmoſt, and began to despair, they it
seems saw me by the help of their Perspeċtive-Glasses,
and that it was some *European* Boat, which as they sup-

posed mu&t belong to some Ship that was lo&t, so they shortned Sail to let me come up. I was encouraged with this, and as I had my Patroon's Antient on Board, I made a Waft of it to them for a Signal of Di&tress, and fir'd a Gun, both which they saw, for they told me they saw the Smoke, tho' they did not hear the Gun; upon these Signals they very kindly brought too, and lay by for me, and in about three Hours time I came up with them.

They ask'd me what I was, in *Portuguese*, and in *Spanish*, and in *French*, but I under&tood none of them; but at la&t a *Scots* Sailor who was on board, call'd to me, and I answer'd him, and told him I was an *Englishman*, that I had made my escape out of Slavery from the *Moors* at *Sallee*; then they bad me come on board, and very kindly took me in, and all my Goods.

It was an inexpressible Joy to me, that any one will believe, that I was thus deliver'd, as I e&teem'd it, from such a miserable and almo&t hopeless Condition as I was in, and I immediately offered all I had to the Captain of the Ship, as a Return for my Deliverance; but he generously told me, he would take nothing from me, but that all I had should be deliver'd safe to me when I came to the *Brasils*, for says he, *I have sav'd your Life on no other Terms than I would be glad to be saved my self, and it may one time or other be my Lot to be taken up in the same Condition*; besides, said he, *when I carry you to the* Brasils, *so great a way from your own Country, if I should take from you what you have, you will be &tarved there, and then I only take away that Life I have given. No, no, Seignor* Inglese, says he, *Mr.* Englishman, *I will carry you thither in Charity, and those things will help you to buy your Subsi&tance there and your Passage home again.*

As he was Charitable in his Proposal, so he was Ju&t in

the Performance to a tittle, for he ordered the Seamen
that none should offer to touch any thing I had; then he
took every thing into his own Possession, and gave me
back an exact Inventory of them, that I might have them,
even so much as my three Earthen Jarrs.

As to my Boat it was a very good one, and that he saw,
and told me he would buy it of me for the Ship's use, and
ask'd me what I would have for it? I told him he had been
so generous to me in every thing, that I could not offer to
make any Price of the Boat, but left it entirely to him, upon which he told me he would give me a Note of his Hand
to pay me 80 Pieces of Eight for it at *Brasil*, and when it
came there, if any one offer'd to give more he would make
it up; he offer'd me also 60 Pieces of Eight more for my
Boy *Xury*, which I was loath to take, not that I was not
willing to let the Captain have him, but I was very loath
to sell the poor Boy's Liberty, who had assisted me so
faithfully in procuring my own. However when I let him
know my Reason, he own'd it to be just, and offer'd me
this Medium, that he would give the Boy an Obligation
to set him free in ten Years, if he turn'd Christian; upon
this, and *Xury* saying he was willing to go to him, I let the
Captain have him.

We had a very good Voyage to the *Brasils*, and arriv'd
in the *Bay de Todos los Santos*, or *All-Saints Bay*, in about
Twenty-two Days after. And now I was once more deliver'd from the most miserable of all Conditions of Life,
and what to do next with my self I was now to consider.

The generous Treatment the Captain gave me, I can
never enough remember; he would take nothing of me
for my Passage, gave me twenty Ducats for the Leopard's
Skin, and forty for the Lyon's Skin which I had in my
Boat, and caused every thing I had in the Ship to be punc-

tually deliver'd me, and what I was willing to sell he bought, such as the Case of Bottles, two of my Guns, and a Piece of the Lump of Bees-wax, for I had made Candles of the rest; in a word, I made about 220 Pieces of Eight of all my Cargo, and with this Stock I went on Shoar in the *Brasils.*

I had not been long here, but being recommended to the House of a good honest Man like himself, who had an *Ingenio* as they call it; that is, a Plantation and a Sugar-House. I lived with him some time, and acquainted my self by that means with the Manner of their planting and making of Sugar; and seeing how well the Planters liv'd, and how they grew rich suddenly, I resolv'd, if I could get Licence to settle there, I would turn Planter among them, resolving in the mean time to find out some Way to get my Money which I had left in *London* remitted to me. To this Purpose getting a kind of a Letter of Naturalization, I purchased as much Land that was Uncur'd, as my Money would reach, and form'd a Plan for my Plantation and Settlement, and such a one as might be suitable to the Stock which I proposed to myself to receive from *England.*

I had a Neighbour, a *Portugueze* of *Lisbon,* but born of *English* Parents, whose Name was *Wells,* and in much such Circumstances as I was. I call him my Neighbour, because his Plantation lay next to mine, and we went on very sociably together. My Stock was but low as well as his; and we rather planted for Food than any thing else, for about two Years. However, we began to increase, and our Land began to come into Order; so that the third Year we planted some Tobacco, and made each of us a large Piece of Ground ready for planting Canes in the Year to come; but we both wanted Help, and now I

found more than before, I had done wrong in parting with
with my Boy *Xury.*

But alas! for me to do wrong that never did right, was
no great Wonder: I had no Remedy but to go on; I was
gotten into an Employment quite remote to my Genius,
and directly contrary to the Life I delighted in, and for
which I forsook my Father's House, and broke thro' all
his good Advice; nay, I was coming into the very Middle
Station, or upper Degree of low Life, which my Father
advised me to before; and which if I resolved to go on
with, I might as well ha' staid at Home, and never have
fatigu'd my self in the World as I had done; and I used
often to say to my self, I could ha' done this as well in
England among my Friends, as ha' gone 5000 Miles off
to do it among Strangers and Salvages in a Wilderness,
and at such a Distance, as never to hear from any Part of
the World that had the least Knowledge of me.

In this manner I used to look upon my Condition with
the utmost Regret. I had no body to converse with but
now and then this Neighbour; no Work to be done, but
by the Labour of my Hands; and I used to say, I liv'd
just like a Man cast away upon some desolate Island, that
had no body there but himself. But how just has it been,
and how should all Men reflect, that when they compare
their present Conditions with others that are worse, Heaven may oblige them to make the Exchange, and be convinc'd of their former Felicity by their Experience: I say,
how just has it been, that the truly solitary Life I reflected
on in an Island of meer Desolation should be my Lot, who
had so often unjustly compar'd it with the Life which I
then led, in which had I continued, I had in all Probability been exceeding prosperous and rich.

I was in some Degree settled in my Measures for carrying on the Plantation, before my kind Friend the Captain of the Ship that took me up at Sea, went back; for the Ship remained there in providing his Loading, and preparing for his Voyage, near three Months, when telling him what little Stock I had left behind me in *London*, he gave me this friendly and sincere Advice, *Seignior Inglese says he*; for so he always called me, if you will give me Letters, and a Procuration here in Form to me, with Orders to the Person who has your Money in *London*, to send your Effeᶜts to *Lisbon*, to such Persons as I shall direᶜt, and in such Goods as are proper for this Country, I will bring you the Produce of them, God willing, at my Return; but since human Affairs are all subjeᶜt to Changes and Disaſters, I would have you give Orders but for One Hundred Pounds *Sterl.* which you say is Half your Stock, and let the Hazard be run for the firſt; so that if it come safe, you may order the reſt the same Way; and if it miscarry, you may have the other Half to have Recourse to for your Supply.

This was so wholesom Advice, and look'd so friendly, that I could not but be convinc'd it was the beſt Course I could take; so I accordingly prepared Letters to the Gentlewoman with whom I had left my Money, and a Procuration to the *Portuguese* Captain, as he desired.

I wrote the *English* Captain's Widow a full Account of all my Adventures, my Slavery, Escape, and how I had met with the *Portugal* Captain at Sea, the Humanity of his Behaviour, and in what Condition I was now in, with all other necessary Direᶜtions for my Supply; and when this honeſt Captain came to *Lisbon*, he found means by some of the *English* Merchants there, to send over not the Order only, but a full Account of my Story to a Merchant at *London*, who represented it effeᶜtually to her;

whereupon, she not only delivered the Money, but out of her own Pocket sent the *Portugal* Captain a very handsom Present for his Humanity and Charity to me.

The Merchant in *London* vesting this Hundred Pounds in *English* Goods, such as the Captain had writ for, sent them directly to him at *Lisbon*, and he brought them all safe to me to the *Brasils*, among which, without my Direction (for I was too young in my Business to think of them) he had taken Care to have all Sorts of Tools, Iron-Work, and Utensils necessary for my Plantation, and which were of great Use to me.

When this Cargo arrived, I thought my Fortunes made, for I was surprised with the Joy of it; and my good Steward the Captain had laid out the Five Pounds which my Friend had sent him for a Present for himself, to purchase, and bring me over a Servant under Bond for six Years Service, and would not accept of any Consideration, except a little Tobacco, which I would have him accept, being of my own Produce.

Neither was this all; but my Goods being all *English* Manufactures, such as Cloath, Stuffs, Bays, and things particularly valuable and desirable in the Country, I found means to sell them to a very great Advantage; so that I might say, I had more than four times the Value of my first Cargo, and was now infinitely beyond my poor Neighbour, I mean in the Advancement of my Plantation; for the first thing I did, I bought me a Negro Slave, and an *European* Servant also; I mean another besides that which the Captain brought me from *Lisbon*.

But as abus'd Prosperity is oftentimes made the very Means of our greatest Adversity, so was it with me. I went on the next Year with great Success in my Plantation: I raised fifty great Rolls of Tobacco on my own

Ground, more than I had disposed of for Necessaries among my Neighbours; and these fifty Rolls being each of above a 100 *Wt.* were well cur'd and laid by against the Return of the Fleet from *Lisbon*: and now increasing in Business and in Wealth, my Head began to be full of Projects and Undertakings beyond my Reach; such as are indeed often the Ruine of the best Heads in Business.

Had I continued in the Station I was now in, I had room for all the happy things to have yet befallen me, for which my Father so earnestly recommended a quiet retired Life, and of which he had so sensibly describ'd the middle Station of Life to be full of; but other things attended me, and I was still to be the wilful Agent of all my own Miseries; and particularly to encrease my Fault and double the Reflections upon my self, which in my future Sorrows I should have leisure to make; all these Miscarriages were procured by my apparent obstinate adhering to my foolish inclination of wandring abroad and pursuing that Inclination, in contradiction to the clearest Views of doing my self good in a fair and plain pursuit of those Prospects and those measures of Life, which Nature and Providence concurred to present me with, and to make my Duty.

As I had once done thus in my breaking away from my Parents, so I could not be content now, but I must go and leave the happy View I had of being a rich and thriving Man in my new Plantation, only to pursue a rash and immoderate Desire of rising faster than the Nature of the Thing admitted; and thus I cast my self down again into the deepest Gulph of human Misery that ever Man fell into, or perhaps could be consistent with Life and a State of Health in the World.

To come then by the just Degrees, to the Particulars

of this Part of my Story; you may suppose, that having
now lived almoſt four Years in the *Brasils*, and beginning
to thrive and prosper very well upon my Plantation; I
had not only learn'd the language, but had contraćted
Acquaintance and Friendship among my Fellow-Plan-
ters, as well as among the Merchants at St. *Salvadore*,
which was our Port; and that in my Discourses among
them, I had frequently given them an Account of my
two Voyages to the Coaſt of *Guinea*, the manner of
Trading with the *Negroes* there, and how easy it was to
purchase upon the Coaſt, for Trifles, such as Beads, Toys,
Knives, Scissars, Hatchets, bits of Glass, and the like;
not only Gold Duſt, *Guinea* Grains, Elephants Teeth,
&c. but *Negroes*, for the Service of the *Brasils*, in great
Numbers.

They liſtened always very attentively to my Discourses
on these Heads, but especially to that Part which related
to the buying *Negroes*, which was a Trade at that time not
only not far entred into, but as far as it was, had been carried on by the Assiento's, or Permission of the Kings of
Spain and *Portugal*, and engross'd in the Publick, so that
few *Negroes* were brought, and those excessive dear.

It happen'd, being in Company with some Merchants
and Planters of my Acquaintance, and talking of those
things very earneſtly, three of them came to me the next
Morning, and told me they had been musing very much
upon what I had discoursed with them of, the laſt Night,
and they came to make a secret Proposal to me; and after
enjoining me Secrecy, they told me, that they had a mind
to fit out a Ship to go to *Guinea*, that they had all Plantations as well as I, and were ſtraiten'd for nothing so much
as Servants; that as it was a Trade that could not be carried on, because they could not publickly sell the *Negroes*

when they came home, so they desired to make but one Voyage, to bring the *Negroes* on Shoar privately, and divide them among their own Plantations; and in a Word, the Question was, whether I would go their Super-Cargo in the Ship to manage the Trading Part upon the Coast of *Guinea?* And they offer'd me that I should have my equal Share of the *Negroes* without providing any Part of the Stock.

This was a fair Proposal it must be confess'd, had it been made to any one that had not had a Settlement and Plantation of his own to look after, which was in a fair way of coming to be very Considerable, and with a good Stock upon it. But for me that was thus entered and established, and had nothing to do but go on as I had begun for three or four Years more, and to have sent for the other hundred Pound from *England,* and who in that time, and with that little Addition, could scarce ha' fail'd of being worth three or four thousand Pounds Sterling, and that encreasing too; for me to think of such a Voyage, was the most preposterous Thing that ever Man in such Circumstances could be guilty of.

But I that was born to be my own Destroyer, could no more resist the Offer than I could restrain my first rambling Designs, when my Father's good Counsel was lost upon me. In a word, I told them I would go with all my Heart, if they would undertake to look after my Plantation in my Absence, and would dispose of it to such as I should direct if I miscarry'd. This they all engag'd to do, and entred into Writings or Covenants to do so ; and I made a formal Will, disposing of my Plantation and Effects, in Case of my Death, making the Captain of the Ship that had sav'd my Life, as before, my universal Heir, but obliging him to dispose of my Effects as I had directed in my Will, one half of the Produce being to himself, and the other to be ship'd to *England*.

In short, I took all possible Caution to preserve my Effects, and keep up my Plantation; had I used half as much Prudence to have look'd into my own Intrest, and have made a Judgment of what I ought to have done, and not to have done, I had certainly never gone away from so prosperous an Undertaking, leaving all the probable Views of a thriving Circumstance, and gone upon a Voyage to Sea, attended with all its common Hazards; to say nothing of the Reasons I had to expect particular Misfortunes to my self.

But I was hurried on, and obey'd blindly the Dictates of my Fancy rather than my Reason; and accordingly the Ship being fitted out, and the Cargo furnished, and all things done as by Agreement, by my Partners in the Voyage, I went on Board in an evil Hour, the first of *September*, 1659, being the same Day eight Year that I went from my Father and Mother at *Hull*, in order to act the Rebel to their Authority, and the Fool to my own Interest.

Our Ship was about 120 Tun Burthen, carried 6 Guns, and 14 Men, besides the Master, his Boy, and my self; we had on board no large Cargo of Goods, except of such Toys as were fit for our Trade with the *Negroes*, such as Beads, bits of Glass, Shells, and odd Trifles, especially little Looking-Glasses, Knives, Scissars, Hatchets, and the like.

The same Day I went on board we set sail, standing away to the Northward upon our own Coast, with Design to stretch over for the *Affrican* Coast, when they came about 10 or 12 Degrees of Northern Latitude, which it seems was the manner of their Course in those Days. We had very good Weather, only excessive hot, all the way upon our own Coast, till we came the Height of *Cape St. Augustino,* from whence keeping farther off at Sea we lost Sight of Land, and steer'd as if we was bound for the Isle *Fernand de Noronha* holding our Course *N.E.* by *N.* and leaving those Isles on the East; in this Course we past the Line in about 12 Days time, and were by our last Observation in 7 Degrees 22 Min. Northern Latitude, when a violent Tournado or Hurricane took us quite out of our Knowledge; it began from the South-East, came about to the North-West, and then settled into the North-East, from whence it blew in such a terrible manner, that for twelve Days together we could do nothing but drive, and scudding away before it, let it carry us whither ever Fate and the Fury of the Winds directed; and during these twelve days, I need not say, that I expected every Day to be swallowed up, nor indeed did any in the Ship expect to save their Lives.

In this Distress, we had besides the Terror of the Storm, one of our Men dyed of the Calenture, and one Man and the Boy wash'd over board; about the 12th Day the Weather abating a little, the Master made an Observation as well as he could, and found that he was in about 11 Degrees North Latitude, but that he was 22 Degrees of Longitude difference West from *Cape* St. *Augustino*; so that he found he was gotten upon the Coast of *Guinea,* or the North Part of *Brasil,* beyond the River *Amozones,* toward that of the River *Oronoque,* commonly call'd the *Great River,* and began to consult with me what Course he should take, for the Ship was leaky and very much disabled, and he was going directly back to the Coast of *Brasil.*

I was positively against that, and looking over the Charts of the Sea-Coast of *America* with him, we concluded there was no inhabited Country for us to have recourse to, till we came within the Circle of the *Carribbe-Islands*, and therefore resolved to ſtand away for *Barbadoes*,which by keeping off at Sea, to avoid the Indraft of the Bay or Gulph of *Mexico*, we might easily perform, as we hoped, in about fifteen Days Sail; whereas we could not possibly make our Voyage to the Coaſt of *Affrica* without some Assiſtance, both to our Ship and to our selves.

With this Design we chang'd our Course and ſteer'd away *N. W.* by *W.* in order to reach some of our *English Islands,* where I hoped for Relief; but our Voyage was otherwise determined, for being in the Latitude of 12 Deg. 18 Min. a second Storm came upon us, which carry'd us away with the same Impetuosity Weſtward, and drove us so out of the very Way of all humane Commerce, that had all our Lives been saved, as to the Sea, we were rather in Danger of being devoured by Savages than ever returning to our own Country.

In this Diſtress, the Wind ſtill blowing very hard, one of our Men early in the Morning, cry'd out, *Land*; and we had no sooner run out of the Cabbin to look out in hopes of seeing where abouts in the World we were; but the Ship ſtruck upon a Sand, and in a moment her Motion being so ſtopp'd, the Sea broke over her in such a manner, that we expeᶜted we should all have perish'd immediately, and we were immediately driven into our close Quarters to shelter us from the very Foam and Sprye of the Sea.

It is not easy for any one, who has not been in the like Condition, to describe or conceive the Conſternation of Men in such Circumſtances; we knew nothing where we were, or upon what Land it was we were driven, whether an Island or the Main, whether inhabited or not inhabit-

ed; and as the Rage of the Wind was ſtill great, tho' rather
less than at firſt, we could not so much as hope to have the
Ship hold many Minutes without breaking in Pieces, unless the Winds by a kind of Miracle should turn immediately about. In a word, we sat looking upon one another,
and expecting Death every Moment, and every Man acting accordingly, as preparing for another World, for
there was little or nothing more for us to do in this; that
which was our present Comfort, and all the Comfort we
had, was, that contrary to our Expectation the Ship did
not break yet, and that the Maſter said the Wind began
to abate.

Now tho' we thought that the Wind did a little abate,
yet the Ship having thus ſtruck upon the Sand, and ſticking too faſt for us to expect her getting off, we were in a
dreadful Condition indeed, and had nothing to do but to
think of saving our Lives as well as we could; we had a
Boat at our Stern juſt before the Storm, but she was firſt
ſtav'd by dashing againſt the Ship's Rudder, and in the
next Place she broke away, and either sunk or was driven
off to Sea, so there was no hope from her; we had another
Boat on board, but how to get her off into the Sea, was a
doubtful thing; however there was no room to debate, for
we fancy'd the Ship would break in Pieces every Minute,
and some told us she was actually broken already.

In this Diſtress the Mate of our Vessel lays hold of the
Boat, and with the help of the reſt of the Men, they got
her slung over the Ship's-side, and getting all into her, let
go, and committed our selves being Eleven in Number,
to God's Mercy, and the wild Sea; for tho' the Storm was
abated considerably, yet the Sea went dreadful high upon
the Shore, and might well be call'd, *Den wild Zee*, as the
Dutch call the Sea in a Storm.

And now our Case was very dismal indeed; for we all saw plainly, that the Sea went so high, that the Boat could not live, and that we should be inevitably drowned. As to making Sail, we had none, nor, if we had, could we ha' done any thing with it: so we work'd at the Oar towards the Land, tho' with heavy Hearts, like Men going to Execution; for we all knew, that when the Boat came nearer the Shore, she would be dash'd in a Thousand Pieces by the Breach of the Sea. However, we committed our Souls to God in the moſt earneſt Manner, and the Wind driving us towards the Shore, we haſten'd our Deſtruction with our own Hands, pulling as well as we could towards Land.

What the Shore was, whether Rock or Sand, whether Steep or Shoal, we knew not; the only Hope that could rationally give us the leaſt Shadow of Expeᴄtation, was, if we might happen into some Bay or Gulph, or the Mouth of some River, where by great Chance we might have run our Boat in, or got under the Lee of the Land, and perhaps made smooth Water. But there was nothing of this appeared; but as we made nearer and nearer the Shore, the Land look'd more frightful than the Sea.

After we had row'd, or rather driven about a League and a Half, as we reckon'd it, a raging Wave, Mountain-like, came rowling a-ſtern of us, and plainly bad us expeᴄt the *Coup de Grace.* In a word, it took us with such a Fury, that it overset the Boat at once; and separating us as well from the Boat, as from one another, gave us not time hardly to say, O God! for we were all swallowed up in a Moment.

Nothing can describe the Confusion of Thought which I felt when I sunk into the Water; for tho' I swam very well, yet I could not deliver my self from the Waves so as

to draw Breath, till that Wave having driven me, or rather carried me a vaſt Way on towards the Shore, and
having spent it self, went back, and left me upon the Land
almoſt dry, but half-dead with the Water I took in. I had
so much Presence of Mind as well as Breath left, that seeing my self nearer the main Land than I expeɛted, I got
upon my Feet, and endeavoured to make on towards the
Land as faſt as I could, before another Wave should return, and take me up again. But I soon found it was impossible to avoid it; for I saw the Sea come after me as
high as a great Hill, and as furious as an Enemy which I
had no Means or Strength to contend with; my Business
was to hold my Breath, and raise my self upon the Water,
if I could; and so by swimming to preserve my Breathing,
and Pilot my self towards the Shore, if possible; my greateſt Concern now being, that the Sea, as it would carry me
a great Way towards the Shore when it came on, might
not carry me back again with it when it gave back towards the Sea.

The Wave that came upon me again, buried me at
once 20 or 30 Foot deep in its own Body; and I could feel
my self carried with a mighty Force and Swiftness towards the Shore a very great Way; but I held my Breath,
and assiſted my self to swim ſtill forward with all my
Might. I was ready to burſt with holding my Breath,
when, as I felt my self rising up, so to my immediate Relief, I found my Head and Hands shoot out above the
Surface of the Water; and tho' it was not two Seconds of
Time that I could keep my self so, yet it reliev'd me greatly, gave me Breath and new Courage. I was covered again
with Water a good while, but not so long but I held it out;
and finding the Water had spent it self, and began to return, I ſtrook forward againſt the Return of the Waves,

and felt Ground again with my Feet. I ſtood ſtill a few
Moments to recover Breath, and till the Water went from
me, and then took to my Heels, and run with what Strength
I had farther towards the Shore. But neither would this
deliver me from the Fury of the Sea, which came pouring
in after me again, and twice more I was lifted up by the
Waves, and carried forwards as before, the Shore being
very flat.

The laſt Time of these two had well near been fatal to
me; for the Sea having hurried me along as before, landed me, or rather dash'd me againſt a Piece of a Rock, and
that with such Force, as it left me senseless, and indeed
helpless, as to my own Deliverance; for the Blow taking
my Side and Breaſt, beat the Breath as it were quite out of
my Body; and had it returned again immediately, I muſt
have been ſtrangled in the Water; but I recover'd a little
before the return of the Waves, and seeing I should be
cover'd again with the Water, I resolv'd to hold faſt by a
Piece of the Rock, and so to hold my Breath, if possible,
till the Wave went back; now as the Waves were not so
high as at firſt, being nearer Land, I held my Hold till
the Wave abated, and then fetch'd another Run, which
brought me so near the Shore, that the next Wave, tho' it
went over me, yet did not so swallow me up as to carry me
away, and the next run I took, I got to the main Land,
where, to my great Comfort, I clamber'd up the Clifts of
the Shore, and sat me down upon the Grass, free from
Danger, and quite out of the Reach of the Water.

I was now landed, and safe on Shore, and began to look
up and thank God that my Life was sav'd in a Case wherein there was some Minutes before scarce any room to
hope. I believe it is impossible to express to the Life what
the Extasies and Transports of the Soul are, when it is so

sav'd, as I may say, out of the very Grave; and I do not wonder now at that Custom, *viz.* That when a Malefactor who has the Halter about his Neck, is tyed up, and just going to be turn'd off, and has a Reprieve brought to him: I say, I do not wonder that they bring a Surgeon with it, to let him Blood that very Moment they tell him of it, that the Surprise may not drive the Animal Spirits from the Heart, and overwhelm him:

For sudden Joys, like Griefs, confound at first.

I walk'd about on the Shore, lifting up my Hands, and my whole Being, as I may say, wrapt up in the Contemplation of my Deliverance, making a Thousand Gestures and Motions which I cannot describe, reflecting upon all my Comrades that were drown'd, and that there should not be one Soul sav'd but my self; for, as for them, I never saw them afterwards, or any Sign of them, except three of their Hats, one Cap, and two Shoes that were not Fellows.

I cast my Eyes to the stranded Vessel, when the Breach and Froth of the Sea being so big, I could hardly see it, it lay so far off, and considered, Lord! how was it possible I could get on Shore?

After I had solac'd my Mind with the comfortable Part of my Condition, I began to look round me to see what kind of Place I was in, and what was next to be done, and I soon found my Comforts abate, and that in a word I had a dreadful Deliverance: For I was wet, had no Clothes to shift me, nor any thing either to eat or drink to comfort me, neither did I see any Prospect before me, but that of perishing with Hunger, or being devour'd by wild Beasts; and that which was particularly afflicting to me, was, that I had no Weapon either to hunt and kill any Creature for my Sustenance, or to defend my self against any other Creature that might desire to kill me for theirs: In a Word, I had nothing about me but a Knife, a Tobacco-pipe, and a little Tobacco in a Box, this was all my Provision, and this threw me into terrible Agonies of Mind, that for a while I run about like a Mad-man; Night coming upon me, I began with a heavy Heart to consider what would be my Lot if there were any ravenous Beasts in that Country, seeing at Night they always come abroad for their Prey.

All the Remedy that offer'd to my Thoughts at that Time, was, to get up into a thick bushy Tree like a Firr, but thorny, which grew near me, and where I resolv'd to sit all Night, and consider the next Day what Death I should dye, for as yet I saw no Prospect of Life; I walk'd about a Furlong from the Shore, to see if I could find any fresh Water to drink, which I did, to my great Joy; and having drank and put a little Tobacco in my Mouth to prevent Hunger, I went to the Tree, and getting up into it, endeavour'd to place my self so, as that if I should sleep I might not fall; and having cut me a short Stick, like a Truncheon, for my Defence, I took up my Lodging, and having been excessively fatigu'd, I fell fast asleep, and slept as comfortably as, I believe, few could have done in my Condition, and found my self the most refresh'd with it, that I think I ever was on such an Occasion.

When I wak'd it was broad Day, the Weather clear, and the Storm abated, so that the Sea did not rage and swell as before: But that which surpris'd me most, was, that the Ship was lifted off in the Night from the Sand where she lay, by the Swelling of the Tyde, and was driven up almost as far as the Rock which I first mention'd, where I had been so bruis'd by the dashing me against it; this being within about a Mile from the Shore where I was, and the Ship seeming to stand upright still, I wish'd my self on board, that, at least, I might save some necessary things for my use.

When I came down from my Appartment in the Tree, I look'd about me again, and the first thing I found was the Boat, which lay as the Wind and the Sea had toss'd her up upon the Land, about two Miles on my right Hand. I walk'd as far as I could upon the Shore to have got to her, but found a Neck or Inlet of Water between me and the Boat, which was about half a Mile broad, so I came back for the present, being more intent upon getting at the Ship, where I hop'd to find something for my present Subsistence.

A little after Noon I found the Sea very calm, and the Tyde ebb'd so far out, that I could come within a Quarter of a Mile of the Ship; and here I found a fresh renewing of my Grief, for I saw evidently, that if we had kept on board, we had been all safe, that is to say, we had all got safe on Shore, and I had not been so miserable as to be left entirely destitute of all Comfort and Company, as I now was; this forc'd Tears from my Eyes again, but as there was little Relief in that, I resolv'd, if possible, to get to the Ship, so I pull'd off my Clothes, for the Weather was hot to Extremity, and took the Water, but when I came to the Ship, my Difficulty was still greater to know how to get on board, for as she lay a ground, and high out of the Water, there was nothing within my Reach to lay hold of, I swam round her twice, and the second Time I spy'd a small Piece of a Rope, which I wonder'd I did not see at first, hang down by the Fore-Chains so low, as that with great Difficulty I got hold of it, and by the help of that Rope, got up into the Forecastle of the Ship, here I found that the Ship was bulg'd, and had a great deal of

Water in her Hold, but that she lay so on the Side of a
Bank of hard Sand, or rather Earth, that her Stern lay
lifted up upon the Bank, and her Head low almoſt to the
Water; by this Means all her Quarter was free, and all
that was in that Part was dry; for you may be sure my firſt
Work was to search and to see what was spoil'd and what
was free; and firſt I found that all the Ship's Provisions
were dry and untouch'd by the Water, and being very
well dispos'd to eat, I went to the Bread-room and fill'd
my Pockets with Bisket, and eat it as I went about other
things, for I had no time to lose; I also found some Rum
in the great Cabbin, of which I took a large Dram, and
which I had indeed need enough of to spirit me for what
was before me: Now I wanted nothing but a Boat to furnish my self with many things which I foresaw would be
very necessary to me.

It was in vain to sit ſtill and wish for what was not to be
had, and this Extremity rouz'd my Application; we had
several spare Yards, and two or three large sparrs of
Wood, and a spare Top-maſt or two in the Ship; I resolv'd to fall to work with these, and I flung as many of
them over board as I could manage for their Weight,
tying every one with a Rope that they might not drive
away; when this was done I went down the Ship's Side,
and pulling them to me, I ty'd four of them faſt together
at both Ends as well as I could, in the Form of a Raft, and
laying two or three short Pieces of Plank upon them cross-
ways, I found I could walk upon it very well, but that it
was not able to bear any great Weight, the Pieces being
too light; so I went to work, and with the Carpenter's Saw
I cut a spare Top-maſt into three Lengths, and added
them to my Raft, with a great deal of Labour and Pains,
but hope of furnishing my self with Necessaries, en-

courag'd me to go beyond what I should have been able
to have done upon another Occasion.

My Raft was now ſtrong enough to bear any reasonable Weight; my next Care was what to load it with, and
how to preserve what I laid upon it from the Surf of the
Sea; But I was not long considering this, I firſt laid all the
Planks or Boards upon it that I could get, and having
consider'd well what I moſt wanted, I firſt got three of
the Seamens Cheſts, which I had broken open and empty'd, and lower'd them down upon my Raft; the firſt of
these I fill'd with Provision, *viz.* Bread, Rice, three
Dutch Cheeses, five Pieces of dry'd Goat's Flesh, which we
liv'd much upon, and a little Remainder of *European* Corn
which had been laid by for some Fowls which we brought
to Sea with us, but the Fowls were kill'd, there had been
some Barly and Wheat together, but, to my great Disap-
pointment, I found afterwards that the Rats had eaten or
spoil'd it all; as for Liquors, I found several Cases of Bottles belonging to our Skipper, in which were some Cordial Waters, and in all about five or six Gallons of Rack,
these I ſtow'd by themselves, there being no need to put
them into the Cheſt, nor no room for them. While I was
doing this, I found the Tyde began to flow, tho' very
calm, and I had the Mortification to see my Coat, Shirt,
and Waſt-coat which I had left on Shore upon the Sand,
swim away; as for my Breeches which were only Linnen
and open knee'd, I swam on board in them and my
Stockings: However this put me upon rummaging for
Clothes, of which I found enough, but took no more than
I wanted for present use, for I had other things which my
Eye was more upon, as firſt Tools to work with on Shore,
and it was after long searching that I found out the Carpenter's Cheſt, which was indeed a very useful Prize to

me, and much more valuable than a Ship Loading of Gold would have been at that time; I got it down to my Raft, even whole as it was, without losing time to look into it, for I knew in general what it contain'd.

My next Care was for some Ammunition and Arms; there were two very good Fowling-pieces in the great Cabbin, and two Pistols, these I secur'd first, with some Powder-horns, and a small Bag of Shot, and two old rusty Swords; I knew there were three Barrels of Powder in the Ship, but knew not where our Gunner had stow'd them, but with much search I found them, two of them dry and good, the third had taken Water, those two I got to my Raft, with the Arms, and now I thought my self pretty well freighted, and began to think how I should get to Shore with them, having neither Sail, Oar, or Rudder, and the least Cap full of Wind would have overset all my Navigation.

I had three Encouragements, 1. A smooth calm Sea, 2. The Tide rising and setting in to the Shore, 3. What little Wind there was blew me towards the Land; and thus, having found two or three broken Oars belonging to the Boat, and besides the Tools which were in the Chest, I found two Saws, an Axe, and a Hammer, and with this Cargo I put to Sea: For a Mile, or thereabouts, my Raft went very well, only that I found it drive a little distant from the Place where I had landed before, by which I perceiv'd that there was some Indraft of the Water, and consequently I hop'd to find some Creek or River there, which I might make use of as a Port to get to Land with my Cargo.

As I imagin'd, so it was, there appear'd before me a little opening of the Land, and I found a strong Current of the Tide set into it, so I guided my Raft as well as I

could to keep in the Middle of the Stream: But here I
had like to have suffer'd a second Shipwreck, which, if I
had, I think verily would have broke my Heart, for knowing nothing of the Coast, my Raft run a-ground at one
End of it upon a Shoal, and not being a-ground at the
other End, it wanted but a little that all my Cargo had
slip'd off towards that End that was a-float, and so fall'n
into the Water: I did my utmost by setting my Back
against the Chests, to keep them in their Places, but
could not thrust off the Raft with all my Strength, neither
durst I stir from the Posture I was in, but holding up the
Chests with all my Might, stood in that Manner near
half an Hour, in which time the rising of the Water
brought me a little more upon a Level, and a little after,
the Water still rising, my Raft floated again, and I thrust
her off with the Oar I had, into the Channel, and then
driving up higher, I at length found my self in the Mouth
of a little River, with Land on both Sides, and a strong
Current or Tide running up, I look'd on both Sides for a
proper Place to get to Shore, for I was not willing to be
driven too high up the River, hoping in time to see some
Ship at Sea, and therefore resolv'd to place my self as
near the Coast as I could.

At length I spy'd a little Cove on the right Shore of the
Creek, to which with great Pain and Difficulty I guided
my Raft, and at last got so near, as that, reaching Ground
with my Oar, I could thrust her directly in, but here I had
like to have dipt all my Cargo in the Sea again; for that
Shore lying pretty steep, that is to say sloping, there was
no Place to land, but where one End of my Float, if it run
on Shore, would lie so high, and the other sink lower as
before, that it would endanger my Cargo again: All that
I could do, was to wait 'till the Tide was at the highest,

keeping the Raft with my Oar like an Anchor to hold the Side of it faſt to the Shore, near a flat Piece of Ground, which I expeƈted the Water would flow over; and so it did: As soon as I found Water enough, for my Raft drew about a Foot of Water, I thruſt her on upon that flat Piece of Ground, and there faſten'd or mor'd her by ſticking my two broken Oars into the Ground; one on one Side near one End, and one on the other Side near the other End; and thus I lay 'till the Water ebb'd away, and left my Raft and all my Cargoe safe on Shore.

My next Work was to view the Country, and seek a proper Place for my Habitation, and where to ſtow my Goods to secure them from whatever might happen; where I was, I yet knew not, whether on the Continent or on an Island, whether inhabited or not inhabited, whether in Danger of wild Beaſts or not: There was a Hill not above a Mile from me, which rose up very ſteep and high, and which seem'd to over-top some other Hills, which lay as in a Ridge from it northward; I took out one of the fowling Pieces, and one of the Piſtols, and an Horn of Powder, and thus arm'd I travell'd for Discovery up to the Top of that Hill, where after I had with great Labour and Difficulty got to the Top, I saw my Fate to my great Affliƈtion, (*viz.*) that I was in an Island environ'd every Way with the Sea, no Land to be seen, except some Rocks which lay a great Way off, and two small Islands less than this, which lay about three Leagues to the Weſt.

I found also that the Island I was in was barren, and, as I saw good Reason to believe, un-inhabited, except by wild Beaſts, of whom however I saw none, yet I saw Abundance of Fowls, but knew not their Kinds, neither when I kill'd them could I tell what was fit for Food, and what not; at my coming back, I shot at a great Bird which I

saw sitting upon a Tree on the Side of a great Wood, I believe it was the first Gun that had been fir'd there since
the Creation of the World; I had no sooner fir'd, but
from all the Parts of the Wood there arose an innumerable Number of Fowls of many Sorts, making a confus'd
Screaming, and crying every one according to his usual
Note; but not one of them of any Kind that I knew: As
for the Creature I kill'd, I took it to be a Kind of a Hawk,
its Colour and Beak resembling it, but had no Talons or
Claws more than common, its Flesh was Carrion, and fit
for nothing.

Contented with this Discovery, I came back to my
Raft, and fell to Work to bring my Cargoe on Shore,
which took me up the rest of that Day, and what to do
with my self at Night I knew not, nor indeed where to
rest; for I was afraid to lie down on the Ground, not knowing but some wild Beast might devour me, tho', as I afterwards found, there was really no Need for those Fears.

However, as well as I could, I barricado'd my self
round with the Chests and Boards that I had brought on
Shore, and made a Kind of a Hut for that Night's Lodging; as for Food, I yet saw not which Way to supply my
self, except that I had seen two or three Creatures like
Hares run out of the Wood where I shot the Fowl.

I now began to consider, that I might yet get a great
many Things out of the Ship, which would be useful to
me, and particularly some of the Rigging, and Sails, and
such other Things as might come to Land, and I resolv'd
to make another Voyage on Board the Vessel, if possible;
and as I knew that the first Storm that blew must necessarily break her all in Pieces, I resolv'd to set all other
Things apart, 'till I got every Thing out of the Ship that I
could get; then I call'd a Council, that is to say, in my

Thoughts, whether I should take back the Raft, but this
appear'd impracticable; so I resolv'd to go as before,
when the Tide was down, and I did so, only that I stripp'd
before I went from my Hut, having nothing on but a
Chequer'd Shirt, and a Pair of Linnen Drawers, and a
Pair of Pumps on my Feet.

I got on Board the Ship, as before, and prepar'd a second Raft, and having had Experience of the first, I neither made this so unweildy, or loaded it so hard, but yet
I brought away several Things very useful to me; as first,
in the Carpenter's Stores I found two or three Bags full
of Nails and Spikes, a great Skrew-Jack, a Dozen or two
of Hatchets, and above all, that most useful Thing call'd
a Grindstone; all these I secur'd together, with several
Things belonging to the Gunner, particularly two or
three Iron Crows, and two Barrels of Musquet Bullets,
seven Musquets, and another fowling Piece, with some
small Quantity of Powder more; a large Bag full of small
Shot, and a great Roll of Sheet Lead: But this last was so
heavy, I could not hoise it up to get it over the Ship's Side.

Besides these Things, I took all the Mens Cloaths that
I could find, and a spare Fore-top-sail, a Hammock, and
some Bedding; and with this I loaded my second Raft, and
brought them all safe on Shore to my very great Comfort.

I was under some Apprehensions during my Absence
from the Land, that at least my Provisions might be devour'd on Shore; but when I came back, I found no Sign
of any Visitor, only there sat a Creature like a wild Cat
upon one of the Chests, which when I came towards it,
ran away a little Distance, and then stood still; she sat
very compos'd, and unconcern'd, and look'd full in my
Face, as if she had a Mind to be acquainted with me, I
presented my Gun at her, but as she did not understand it,

she was perfectly unconcern'd at it, nor did she offer to
stir away; upon which I toss'd her a Bit of Bisket, tho' by
the Way ˙ was not very free of it, for my Store was not
great: However, I spar'd her a Bit, I say, and she went to
it, smell'd of it, and ate it, and look'd (as pleas'd) for more,
but I thanked her, and could spare no more so she
march'd off.

Having got my second Cargoe on Shore, tho' I was
fain to open the Barrels of Powder, and bring them by
Parcels, for they were too heavy, being large Casks, I
went to work to make me a little Tent with the Sail and
some Poles which I cut for that Purpose, and into this
Tent I brought every Thing that I knew would spoil,
either with Rain or Sun, and I piled all the empty Chests
and Casks up in a Circle round the Tent, to fortify it from
any sudden Attempt, either from Man or Beast.

When I had done this I block'd up the Door of the
Tent with some Boards within, and an empty Chest set
up on End without, and spreading one of the Beds upon
the Ground, laying my two Pistols just at my Head, and
my Gun at Length by me, I went to Bed for the first Time,
and slept very quietly all Night, for I was very weary and
heavy, for the Night before I had slept little, and had labour'd very hard all Day, as well to fetch all those Things
from the Ship, as to get them on Shore.

I had the biggest Maggazin of all Kinds now that ever
were laid up, I believe, for one Man, but I was not satisfy'd still; for while the Ship sat upright in that Posture, I
thought I ought to get every Thing out of her that I
could; so every Day at low Water I went on Board, and
brought away some Thing or other: But particularly the
third Time I went, I brought away as much of the Rigging as I could, as also all the small Ropes and Rope-twine

I could get, with a Piece of spare Canvass, which was to
mend the Sails upon Occasion, the Barrel of wet Gun-
powder: In a Word, I brought away all the Sails first and
last, only that I was fain to cut them in Pieces, and bring
as much at a Time as I could; for they were no more useful to be Sails, but as meer Canvass only.

But that which comforted me more still was, that at
last of all, after I had made five or six such Voyages as
these, and thought I had nothing more to expect from the
Ship that was worth my medling with, I say, after all this,
I found a great Hogshead of Bread and three large Runlets of Rum or Spirits, and a Box of Sugar, and a Barrel of
fine Flower; this was surprizing to me, because I had
given over expecting any more Provisions, except what
was spoil'd by the Water: I soon empty'd the Hogshead
of that Bread, and wrapt it up Parcel by Parcel in Pieces
of the Sails, which I cut out; and in a Word, I got all this
safe on Shore also.

The next Day I made another Voyage; and now having plunder'd the Ship of what was portable and fit to
hand out, I began with the Cables; and cutting the great
Cable into Pieces, such as I could move, I got two Cables
and a Hawser on Shore, with all the Iron Work I could
get; and having cut down the Spritsail-yard, and the Mis-
sen-yard, and every Thing I could to make a large Raft, I
loaded it with all those heavy Goods, and came away:
But my good Luck began now to leave me; for this Raft
was so unweildy, and so overloaden, that after I was enter'd the little Cove, where I had landed the rest of my
Goods, not being able to guide it so handily as I did the
other, it overset, and threw me and all my Cargoe into the
Water; as for my self it was no great Harm, for I was near
the Shore; but as to my Cargoe, it was great Part of it lost,

especially the Iron, which I expected would have been of great Use to me: However, when the Tide was out, I got most of the Pieces of Cable ashore, and some of the Iron, tho' with infinite Labour; for I was fain to dip for it into the Water, a Work which fatigu'd me very much: After this I went every Day on Board, and brought away what I could get.

I had been now thirteen Days on Shore, and had been eleven Times on Board the Ship; in which Time I had brought away all that one Pair of Hands could well be suppos'd capable to bring, tho' I believe verily, had the calm Weather held, I should have brought away the whole Ship Piece by Piece: But preparing the 12th Time to go on Board, I found the Wind begin to rise; however at low Water I went on Board, and tho' I thought I had rumag'd the Cabbin so effectually, as that nothing more could be found, yet I discover'd a Locker with Drawers in it, in one of which I found two or three Razors, and one Pair of large Sizzers, with some ten or a Dozen of good Knives and Forks; in another I found about Thirty six Pounds value in Money, some *European* Coin, some *Brasil*, some Pieces of Eight, some Gold, some Silver.

I smil'd to my self at the Sight of this Money, O Drug! Said I aloud, what art thou good for, Thou art not worth to me, no not the taking off of the Ground, one of those Knives is worth all this Heap, I have no Manner of use for thee, e'en remain where thou art, and go to the Bottom as a Creature whose Life is not worth saving. However, upon Second Thoughts, I took it away, and wrapping all this in a Piece of Canvas, I began to think of making another Raft, but while I was preparing this, I found the Sky over-cast, and the Wind began to rise, and in a Quarter of an Hour it blew a fresh Gale from the Shore;

it presently occur'd to me, that it was in vain to pretend
to make a Raft with the Wind off Shore, and that it was
my Business to be gone before the Tide of Flood began,
otherwise I might not be able to reach the Shore at all:
Accordingly I let my self down into the Water, and swam
cross the Channel, which lay between the Ship and the
Sands, and even that with Difficulty enough, partly with
the Weight of the Things I had about me, and partly the
Roughness of the Water, for the Wind rose very hastily,
and before it was quite high Water, it blew a Storm.

But I was gotten home to my little Tent, where I lay
with all my Wealth about me very secure. It blew very
hard all that Night, and in the Morning when I look'd
out, behold no more Ship was to be seen; I was a little surpriz'd, but recover'd my self with this satisfactory Reflection, *viz.* That I had lost no time, nor abated no Dilli-
gence to get every thing out of her that could be useful to
me, and that indeed there was little left in her that I was
able to bring away if I had had more time.

I now gave over any more Thoughts of the Ship, or of
any thing out of her, except what might drive on Shore
from her Wreck, as indeed divers Pieces of her afterwards did; but those things were of small use to me.

My Thoughts were now wholly employ'd about se-
curing my self against either Savages, if any should appear, or wild Beasts, if any were in the Island; and I had
many Thoughts of the Method how to do this, and what
kind of Dwelling to make, whether I should make me a
Cave in the Earth, or a Tent upon the Earth: And, in
short, I resolv'd upon both, the Manner and Discription
of which, it may not be improper to give an Account of.

I soon found the Place I was in was not for my Settlement, particularly because it was upon a low moorish

Ground near the Sea, and I believ'd would not be whol-
some, and more particularly because there was no fresh
Water near it, so I resolv'd to find a more healthy and
more convenient Spot of Ground.

I consulted several Things in my Situation which I
found would be proper for me, 1st. Health, and fresh
Water I just now mention'd, 2dly. Shelter from the Heat
of the Sun, 3dly. Security from ravenous Creatures, whether Men or Beasts, 4thly. a View to the Sea, that if God
sent any Ship in Sight, I might not lose any Advantage
for my Deliverance, of which I was not willing to banish
all my Expectation yet.

In search of a Place proper for this, I found a little
Plain on the Side of a rising Hill, whose Front towards
this little Plain, was steep as a House-side, so that nothing could come down upon me from the Top; on the
Side of this Rock there was a hollow Place worn a little
way in like the Entrance or Door of a Cave, but there was
not really any Cave or Way into the Rock at all.

On the Flat of the Green, just before this hollow Place,
I resolv'd to pitch my Tent: This Plain was not above
an Hundred Yards broad, and about twice as long, and
lay like a Green before my Door, and at the End of it
descended irregularly every Way down into the Low-
grounds by the Sea side. It was on the *N. N. W.* Side of
the Hill, so that I was shelter'd from the Heat every Day,
till it came to a *W.* and by *S.* Sun, or thereabouts, which
in those Countries is near the Setting.

Before I set up my Tent, I drew a half Circle before
the hollow Place, which took in about Ten Yards in its
Semi-diameter from the Rock, and Twenty Yards in its
Diameter, from its Beginning and Ending.

In this half Circle I pitch'd two Rows of strong Stakes,

driving them into the Ground till they stood very firm like
Piles, the biggest End being out of the Ground about
Five Foot and a Half, and sharpen'd on the Top: The
two Rows did not stand above Six Inches from one another.

Then I took the Pieces of Cable which I had cut in the
Ship, and I laid them in Rows one upon another, within
the Circle, between these two Rows of Stakes, up to the
Top, placing other Stakes in the In-side, leaning against
them, about two Foot and a half high, like a Spurr to a
Post, and this Fence was so strong, that neither Man or
Beast could get into it or over it: This cost me a great deal
of Time and Labour, especially to cut the Piles in the
Woods, bring them to the place, and drive them into the
Earth.

The Entrance into this Place I made to be not by a
Door, but by a short Ladder to go over the Top, which
Ladder, when I was in, I lifted over after me, and so I was
compleatly fenc'd in, and fortify'd, as I thought, from all
the World, and consequently slept secure in the Night,
which otherwise I could not have done, tho', as it appear'd afterward, there was no need of all this Caution
from the Enemies that I apprehended Danger from.

Into this Fence or Fortress, with infinite Labour, I
carry'd all my Riches, all my Provisions, Ammunition
and Stores, of which you have the Account above, and I
made me a large Tent, which, to preserve me from the
Rains that in one Part of the Year are very violent there,
I made double, *viz.* One smaller Tent within, and one
larger Tent above it, and cover'd the uppermost with a
large Tarpaulin which I had sav'd among the Sails.

And now I lay no more for a while in the Bed which I
had brought on Shore, but in a Hammock, which was in-

deed a very good one, and belong'd to the Mate of the
Ship.

Into this Tent I brought all my Provisions, and every
thing that would spoil by the Wet, and having thus enclos'd all my Goods, I made up the Entrance, which till
now I had left open, and so pass'd and re-pass'd, as I said
by a short Ladder.

When I had done this, I began to work my Way into
the Rock, and bringing all the Earth and Stones that I
dug down out thro' my Tent, I laid 'em up within my
Fence in the Nature of a Terras, that so it rais'd the
Ground within about a Foot and a Half; and thus I made
me a Cave juſt behind my Tent, which serv'd me like a
Cellar to my House.

It coſt me much Labour, and many Days, before all
these Things were brought to Perfeҫtion, and therefore I
muſt go back to some other Things which took up some
of my Thoughts. At the same time it happen'd after I had
laid my Scheme for the setting up my Tent and making
the Cave, that a Storm of Rain falling from a thick dark
Cloud, a sudden Flash of Lightning happen'd, and after
that a great Clap of Thunder, as is naturally the Effeҫt of
it; I was not so much surpris'd with the Lightning as I
was with a Thought which darted into my Mind as swift
as the Lightning it self: O my Powder! My very Heart
sunk within me, when I thought, that at one Blaſt all my
Powder might be deſtroy'd, on which, not my Defence
only, but the providing me Food, as I thought, entirely
depended; I was nothing near so anxious about my own
Danger, tho' had the Powder took fire, I had never known
who had hurt me.

Such Impression did this make upon me, that after the
Storm was over, I laid aside all my Works, my Building,

and Fortifying, and apply'd my self to make Bags and
Boxes to separate the Powder, and keep it a little and a
little in a Parcel, in hope, that whatever might come, it
might not all take Fire at once, and to keep it so apart
that it should not be possible to make one part fire another: I finish'd this Work in about a Fortnight, and I
think my Powder, which in all was about 240 l. weight
was divided in not less than a Hundred Parcels; as to the
Barrel that had been wet, I did not apprehend any Danger from that, so I plac'd it in my new Cave, which in my
Fancy I call'd my Kitchin, and the reſt I hid up and down
in Holes among the Rocks, so that no wet might come to
it, marking very carefully where I laid it.

In the Interval of time while this was doing I went out
once at leaſt every Day with my Gun, as well to divert my
self, as to see if I could kill any thing fit for Food, and as
near as I could to acquaint my self with what the Island
produc'd. The firſt time I went out I presently discover'd
that there were Goats in the Island, which was a great
Satisfaction to me; but then it was attended with this
Misfortune to me, *viz.* That they were so shy, so subtile,
and so swift of Foot, that it was the difficulteſt thing in the
World to come at them: But I was not discourag'd at this,
not doubting but I might now and then shoot one, as it
soon happen'd, for after I had found their Haunts a little,
I laid wait in this Manner for them: I observ'd if they
saw me in the Valleys, tho' they were upon the Rocks,
they would run away as in a terrible Fright; but if they
were feeding in the Valleys, and I was upon the Rocks,
they took no Notice of me, from whence I concluded,
that by the Position of their Opticks, their Sight was so
directed downward, that they did not readily see Objects
that were above them; so afterward I took this Method, I

always clim'd the Rocks firſt to get above them, and then had frequently a fair Mark. The firſt shot I made among these Creatures, I kill'd a She-Goat which had a little Kid by her which she gave Suck to, which griev'd me heartily; but when the Old one fell, the Kid ſtood ſtock ſtill by her till I came and took her up, and not only so, but when I carry'd the Old one with me upon my Shoulders, the Kid follow'd me quite to my Enclosure, upon which I laid down the Dam, and took the Kid in my Arms, and carry'd it over my Pale, in hopes to have bred it up tame, but it would not eat, so I was forc'd to kill it and eat it my self; these two supply'd me with Flesh a great while, for I eat sparingly; and sav'd my Provisions (my Bread especially) as much as possibly I could.

Having now fix'd my Habitation, I found it absolutely necessary to provide a Place to make a Fire in, and Fewel to burn; and what I did for that, as also how I enlarg'd my Cave, and what Conveniences I made, I shall give a full Account of in its Place: But I muſt firſt give some little Account of my self, and of my Thoughts about Living, which it may well be suppos'd were not a few.

I had a dismal Prospeƈt of my Condition, for as I was not caſt away upon that Island without being driven, as is said, by a violent Storm quite out of the Course of our intended Voyage, and a great Way, *viz.* some Hundreds of Leagues out of the ordinary Course of the Trade of Mankind, I had great Reason to consider it as a Determination of Heaven, that in this desolate Place, and in this desolate Manner I should end my Life; the Tears would run plentifully down my Face when I made these Refleƈtions, and sometimes I would expoſtulate with my self, Why Providence should thus compleatly ruine its Creatures, and render them so absolutely miserable, so without Help abandon'd, so entirely depress'd, that it could hardly be rational to be thankful for such a Life.

But something always return'd swift upon me to check these Thoughts, and to reprove me; and particularly one Day walking with my Gun in my Hand by the Sea-side, I was very pensive upon the Subject of my present Condition, when Reason as it were expostulated with me t'other Way, thus : Well, you are in a desolate Condition 'tis true, but pray remember, Where are the rest of you? Did not you come Eleven of you into the Boat, where are the Ten? Why were not they sav'd and you lost? Why were you singled out? Is it better to be here or there, and then I pointed to the Sea? All Evils are to be consider'd with the Good that is in them, and with what worse attends them.

Then it occurr'd to me again, how well I was furnish'd for my Subsistence, and what would have been my Case if it had not happen'd, *Which was an Hundred Thousand to one*, that the Ship floated from the Place where she first struck and was driven so near to the Shore that I had time to get all these Things out of her: What would have been my Case, if I had been to have liv'd in the Condition in which I at first came on Shore, without Necessaries of Life, or Necessaries to supply and procure them? Particularly said I aloud, (tho' to my self) what should I ha' done without a Gun, without Ammunition, without any Tools to make any thing, or to work with, without Clothes, Bedding, a Tent, or any manner of Covering, and that now I had all these to a Sufficient Quantity, and was in a fair way to provide my self in such a manner, as to live without my Gun when my Ammunition was spent; so that I had a tollerable View of subsisting without any Want as long as I liv'd; for I consider'd from the beginning how I would provide for the Accidents that might happen, and for the time that was to come, even not only after my Ammunition should be spent, but even after my Health or Strength should decay.

I confess I had not entertain'd any Notion of my Ammunition being destroy'd at one Blast, I mean my Powder being blown up by Lightning, and this made the Thoughts of it so surprising to me when it lighten'd and thunder'd, as I observ'd just now.

And now being to enter into a melancholy Relation of a Scene of silent Life, such perhaps as was never heard of in the World before, I shall take it from its Beginning, and continue it in its Order. It was, by my Account, the 30th. of *Sept.* when, in the Manner as above said, I first set Foot upon this horrid Island, when the Sun being, to us, in its Autumnal Equinox, was almost just over my Head, for I reckon'd my self, by Observation, to be in the Latitude of 9 Degrees 22 Minutes North of the Line.

After I had been there about Ten or Twelve Days, it came into my Thoughts, that I should lose my Reckoning of Time for want of Books and Pen and Ink, and should even forget the Sabbath Days from the working Days; but to prevent this I cut it with my Knife upon a large Post, in Capital Letters, and making it into a great Cross I set it up on the Shore where I first landed, viz. *I come on Shore here on the 30th of* Sept. 1659. Upon the Sides of this square Post I cut every Day a Notch with my Knife, and every seventh Notch was as long again as the rest, and every first Day of the Month as long again as that long one, and thus I kept my Kalender, or weekly, monthly, and yearly reckoning of Time.

In the next place we are to observe, that among the

many things which I brought out of the Ship in the
several Voyages, which, as above mention'd, I made to it,
I got several things of less Value, but not at all less useful
to me, which I omitted setting down before; as in particular, Pens, Ink, and Paper, several Parcels in the Captain's, Mate's, Gunner's, and Carpenter's keeping, three
or four Compasses, some Mathematical Instruments,
Dials, Perspectives, Charts, and Books of Navigation, all
which I huddled together, whether I might want them or
no; also I found three very good Bibles which came to me
in my Cargo from *England*, and which I had pack'd up
among my things; some *Portugueze* Books also, and
among them two or three Popish Prayer-Books, and several other Books, all which I carefully secur'd. And I
must not forget, that we had in the Ship a Dog and two
Cats, of whose eminent History I may have occasion to
say something in its place; for I carry'd both the Cats with
me, and as for the Dog, he jump'd out of the Ship of himself, and swam on Shore to me the Day after I went on
Shore with my first Cargo, and was a trusty Servant to me
many Years; I wanted nothing that he could fetch me,
nor any Company that he could make up to me, I only
wanted to have him talk to me, but that would not do: As
I observ'd before, I found Pen, Ink and Paper, and I husbanded them to the utmost, and I shall shew, that while
my Ink lasted, I kept things very exact, but after that was
gone I could not, for I could not make any Ink by any
Means that I could devise.

And this put me in mind that I wanted many things,
notwithstanding all that I had amass'd together, and of
these, this of Ink was one, as also Spade, Pick-Axe, and
Shovel to dig or remove the Earth, Needles, Pins, and

Thread; as for Linnen, I soon learn'd to want that without much Difficulty.

This want of Tools made every Work I did go on heavily, and it was near a whole Year before I had entirely finish'd my little Pale or surrounded Habitation: The Piles or Stakes, which were as heavy as I could well lift, were a long time in cutting and preparing in the Woods, and more by far in bringing home, so that I spent some times two Days in cutting and bringing home one of those Poſts, and a third Day in driving it into the Ground; for which Purpose I got a heavy Piece of Wood at firſt, but at laſt bethought my self of one of the Iron Crows, which however tho' I found it, yet it made driving those Poſts or Piles very laborious and tedious Work.

But what need I ha' been concern'd at the Tediousness of any thing I had to do, seeing I had time enough to do it in, nor had I any other Employment if that had been over, at leaſt, that I could foresee, except the ranging the Island to seek for Food, which I did more or less every Day.

I now began to consider seriously my Condition, and the Circumſtance I was reduc'd to, and I drew up the State of my Affairs in Writing, not so much to leave them to any that were to come after me, for I was like to have but few Heirs, as to deliver my Thoughts from daily poring upon them, and afflicting my Mind; and as my Reason began now to maſter my Despondency, I began to comfort my self as well as I could, and to set the good against the Evil, that I might have something to diſtinguish my Case from worse, and I ſtated it very impartially, like Debtor and Creditor, the Comforts I enjoy'd, againſt the Miseries I suffer'd, Thus,

Evil.	Good.
I am cast upon a horrible desolate Island, void of all Hope of Recovery.	*But I am alive, and not drown'd as all my Ship's Company was.*
I am singl'd out and separated, as it were, from all the World to be miserable.	*But I am singl'd out too from all the Ship's Crew to be spar'd from Death; and he that miraculously sav'd me from Death, can deliver me from this Condition.*
I am divided from Mankind, a Solitaire, one banish'd from humane Society.	*But I am not starv'd and perishing on a barren Place, affording no Sustenance.*
I have not Clothes to cover me.	*But I am in a hot Climate, where if I had Clothes I could hardly wear them.*
I am without any Defence or Means to resist any Violence of Man or Beast.	*But I am cast on an Island, where I see no wild Beasts to hurt me, as I saw on the Coast of* Africa: *And what if I had been Shipwreck'd there?*
I have no Soul to speak to, or relieve me.	*But God wonderfully sent the Ship in near enough to the Shore, that I have gotten out so many necessary things as will either supply my Wants, or enable me to supply my self even as long as I live.*

Upon the whole, here was an undoubted Testimony, that there was scarce any Condition in the World so miserable, but there was something *Negative* or something *Positive* to be thankful for in it; and let this stand as a Direction from the Experience of the most miserable of all Conditions in this World, that we may always find in it something to comfort our selves from, and to set in the Description of Good and Evil, on the Credit Side of the Accompt.

Having now brought my Mind a little to relish my Condition, and given over looking out to Sea to see if I could spy a Ship, I say, giving over these things, I began to apply my self to accommodate my way of Living, and to make things as easy to me as I could.

I have already describ'd my Habitation, which was a Tent under the Side of a Rock, surrounded with a strong Pale of Posts and Cables, but I might now rather call it a Wall, for I rais'd a kind of Wall up against it of Turfs, about two Foot thick on the Out-side, and after some time, I think it was a Year and a Half, I rais'd Rafters from it leaning to the Rock, and thatch'd or cover'd it with Bows of Trees, and such things as I could get to keep out the Rain, which I found at some times of the Year very violent.

I have already observ'd how I brought all my Goods into this Pale, and into the Cave which I had made behind me: But I must observe too, that at first this was a confus'd Heap of Goods, which as they lay in no Order, so they took up all my Place, I had no room to turn my self; so I set my self to enlarge my Cave and Works farther into the Earth, for it was a loose sandy Rock, which yielded easily to the Labour I bestow'd on it; and so when I found I was pretty safe as to Beasts of Prey, I work'd side-ways to the Right Hand into the Rock, and then turning to the Right again, work'd quite out and made me a Door to come out, on the Out-side of my Pale or Fortification.

This gave me not only Egress and Regress, as it were a back Way to my Tent and to my Storehouse, but gave me room to ſtow my Goods.

And now I began to apply my self to make such necessary things as I found I moſt wanted, as particularly a Chair and a Table, for without these I was not able to enjoy the few Comforts I had in the World, I could not write, or eat, or do several things which so much Pleasure without a Table.

So I went to work; and here I muſt needs observe, that as Reason is the Subſtance and Original of the Mathematicks, so by ſtating and squaring every thing by Reason, and by making the moſt rational Judgment of things, every Man may be in time Maſter of every mechanick Art. I had never handled a Tool in my Life, and yet in time by Labour, Application, and Contrivance, I found at laſt that I wanted nothing but I could have made it, especially if I had had Tools; however I made abundance of things, even without Tools, and some with no more Tools than an Adze and a Hatchet, which perhaps were never made that way before, and that with infinite Labour: For Example, If I wanted a Board, I had no other Way but to cut down a Tree, set it on an Edge before me, and hew it flat on either Side with my Axe, till I had brought it to be thin as a Plank, and then dubb it smooth with my Adze. It is true, by this Method I could make but one Board out of a whole Tree, but this I had no Remedy for but Patience, any more than I had for the prodigious deal of Time and Labour which it took me up to make a Plank or Board: But my Time or Labour was little worth, and so it was as well employ'd one way as another.

However, I made me a Table and a Chair, as I observ'd above, in the firſt Place, and this I did out of the short Pieces of Boards that I brought on my Raft from the Ship: But when I had wrought out some Boards, as above I made large Shelves of the Breadth of a Foot and a Half one over another, all along one Side of my Cave, to lay all my Tools, Nails, and Iron-work, and in a Word, to separate every thing at large in their Places, that I muſt come easily at them; I knock'd Pieces into the Wall of the Rock to hang my Guns and all things that would hang up.

So that had my Cave been to be seen, it look'd like a general Magazine of all Necessary things, and I had every thing so ready at my Hand, that it was a great Pleasure to me to see all my Goods in such Order, and especially to find my Stock of all Necessaries so great.

And now it was when I began to keep a Journal of every Day's Employment, for indeed at firſt I was in too much Hurry, and not only Hurry as to Labour, but in too much Discomposure of Mind, and my Journal would ha' been full of many dull things: For Example, I muſt have said thus. *Sept.* the 30th. After I got to Shore and had escap'd drowning, inſtead of being thankful to God for my Deliverance, having firſt vomited with the great Quantity of salt Water which was gotten into my Stomach, and recovering my self a little, I ran about the Shore, wringing my Hands and beating my Head and Face, exclaiming at my Misery, and crying out, I was undone, undone, till tyr'd and faint I was forc'd to lye down on the Ground to repose, but durſt not sleep for fear of being devour'd.

Some Days after this, and after I had been on board the

Ship, and got all that I could out of her, yet I could not forbear getting up to the Top of a little Mountain and looking out to Sea in hopes of seeing a Ship, then fancy at a vaſt Diſtance I spy'd a Sail, please my self with the Hopes of it, and then after looking ſteadily till I was almoſt blind, lose it quite, and sit down and weep like a Child, and thus encrease my Misery by my Folly.

But having gotten over these things in some Measure, and having settled my houshold Stuff and Habitation, made me a Table and a Chair, and all as handsome about me as I could, I began to keep my Journal, of which I shall here give you the Copy (tho' in it will be told all these Particulars over again) as long as it laſted, for having no more Ink I was forc'd to leave it off.

The J O U R N A L.

*S*EptEmber 30, 1659. I poor miserable *Robinson Crusoe*, being shipwreck'd, during a dreadful Storm, in the offing, came on Shore on this dismal unfortunate Island, which I call'd *the Island of Despair*, all the reſt of the Ship's Company being drown'd, and my self almoſt dead.

All the reſt of that Day I spent in afflicting my self at the dismal Circumſtances I was brought to, *viz.* I had neither Food, House, Clothes, Weapon, or Place to fly to, and in Despair of any Relief, saw nothing but Death before me, either that I should be devour'd by wild Beaſts, murther'd by Savages, or ſtarv'd to Death for Want of Food. At the Approach of Night, I slept in a Tree for fear of wild Creatures, but slept soundly tho' it rain'd all Night.

Oɥober 1. In the Morning I saw to my great Surprise the Ship had floated with the high Tide, and was driven

on Shore again much nearer the Island, which as it was
some Comfort on one hand, for seeing her sit upright,
and not broken to Pieces, I hop'd, if the Wind abated, I
might get on board, and get some Food and Necessaries
out of her for my Relief; so on the other hand, it renew'd
my Grief at the Loss of my Comrades, who I imagin'd if
we had all ſtaid on board might have sav'd the Ship, or at
leaſt that they would not have been all drown'd as they
were; and that had the Men been sav'd, we might perhaps have built us a Boat out of the Ruins of the Ship, to
have carried us to some other Part of the World. I spent
great Part of this Day in perplexing my self on these
things; but at length seeing the Ship almoſt dry, I went
upon the Sand as near as I could, and then swam on
board; this Day also it continu'd raining, tho' with no
Wind at all.

From the 1ſt of *Oƈober*, to the 24th. All these Days entirely spent in many several Voyages to get all I could out
of the Ship, which I brought on Shore, every Tide of
Flood, upon Rafts. Much Rain also in these Days, tho'
with some Intervals of fair Weather: But, it seems, this
was the rainy Season.

Oƈ. 20. I overset my Raft, and all the Goods I had got
upon it, but being in shoal Water, and the things being
chiefly heavy, I recover'd many of them when the Tide
was out.

Oƈ, 25. It rain'd all Night and all Day, with some
Guſts of Wind, during which time the Ship broke in
Pieces, the Wind blowing a little harder than before, and
was no more to be seen, except the Wreck of her, and that
only at low Water. I spent this Day in covering and secur-
ing the Goods which I had sav'd, that the Rain might not
spoil them.

Oct. 26. I walk'd about the Shore almost all Day to find out a place to fix my Habitation, greatly concern'd to secure my self from an Attack in the Night, either from wild Beasts or Men. Towards Night I fix'd upon a proper Place under a Rock, and mark'd out a Semi-Circle for my Encampment, which I resolv'd to strengthen with a Work, Wall, or Fortification made of double Piles, lin'd within with Cables, and without with Turf.

From the 26th. to the 30th. I work'd very hard in carrying all my Goods to my new Habitation, tho' some Part of the time it rain'd exceeding hard.

The 31st. in the Morning I went out into the Island with my Gun to see for some Food, and discover the Country, when I kill'd a She-Goat, and her Kid follow'd me home, which I afterwards kill'd also because it would not feed.

November 1. I set up my Tent under a Rock, and lay there for the first Night, making it as large as I could with Stakes driven in to swing my Hammock upon.

Nov. 2. I set up all my Chests and Boards, and the Pieces of Timber which made my Rafts, and with them form'd a Fence round me, a little within the Place I had mark'd out for my Fortification.

Nov. 3. I went out with my Gun and kill'd two Fowls like Ducks, which were very good Food. In the Afternoon went to work to make me a Table.

Nov. 4. This Morning I began to order my times of Work, of going out with my Gun, time of Sleep, and time of Diversion, *viz.* Every Morning I walk'd out with my Gun for two or three Hours if it did not rain, then employ'd my self to work till about Eleven a-Clock, then eat what I had to live on, and from Twelve to Two I lay down to sleep, the Weather being excessive hot, and then in the

Evening to work again: The working Part of this Day
and of the next were wholly employ'd in making my Table, for I was yet but a very sorry Workman, tho' Time
and Necessity made me a compleat natural Mechanick
soon after, as I believe it would do any one else.

Nov. 5. This Day went abroad with my Gun and my
Dog, and kill'd a wild Cat, her Skin pretty soft, but her
Flesh good for nothing : Every Creature I kill'd I took
off the Skins and preserv'd them: Coming back by the
Sea Shore, I saw many Sorts of Sea Fowls which I did not
understand, but was surpris'd and almost frighted with
two or three Seals, which, while I was gazing at, not well
knowing what they were, got into the Sea and escap'd me
for that time.

Nov. 6. After my Morning Walk I went to work with
my Table again, and finish'd it, tho' not to my liking; nor
was it long before I learn'd to mend it.

Nov. 7. Now it began to be settled fair Weather. The
7th, 8th, 9th, 10th, and Part of the 12th. (for the 11th.
was Sunday) I took wholly up to make me a Chair, and
with much ado brought it to a tolerable Shape, but never
to please me, and even in the making I pull'd it in Pieces
several times. *Note,* I soon neglected my keeping Sun-
days, for omitting my Mark for them on my Post, I forgot which was which.

Nov. 13. This Day it rain'd, which refresh'd me exceedingly, and cool'd the Earth, but it was accompany'd
with terrible Thunder and Lightning, which frighted me
dreadfully for fear of my Powder; as soon as it was over, I
resolv'd to separate my Stock of Powder into as many little Parcels as possible, that it might not be in Danger.

Nov. 14, 15, 16. These three Days I spent in making
little square Chests or Boxes, which might hold a Pound

or two Pound, at moſt, of Powder, and so putting the
Powder in, I ſtow'd it in Places as secure and remote from
one another as possible. On one of these three Days I
kill'd a large Bird that was good to eat, but I know not
what to call it.

Nov. 17. This Day I began to dig behind my Tent in
to the Rock to make room for my farther Conveniency:
Note, Two Things I wanted exceedingly for this Work
viz. A Pick-axe, a Shovel, and a Wheel-barrow or Basket,
so I desiſted from my Work, and began to consider how
to supply that Want and make me some Tools; as for a
Pick-axe, I made use of the Iron Crows, which were proper enough, tho' heavy; but the next thing was a Shovel
or Spade, this was so absolutely necessary, that indeed I
could do nothing effeftually without it, but what kind of
one to make I knew not.

Nov. 18. The next Day in searching the Woods I found
a Tree of that Wood, or like it, which, in the *Brasils* they
call the *Iron Tree,* for its exceeding Hardness, of this,
with great Labour and almoſt spoiling my Axe, I cut a
Piece, and brought it home too with Difficulty enough,
for it was exceeding heavy.

The excessive Hardness of the Wood, and having no
other Way, made me a long while upon this Machine, for
I work'd it effeftually by little and little into the Form of
a Shovel or Spade, the Handle exaftly shap'd like ours in
England, only that the broad Part having no Iron shod
upon it at Bottom, it would not laſt me so long, however
it serv'd well enough for the uses which I had occasion to
put it to; but never was a Shovel, I believe, made after
that Fashion, or so long a making.

I was ſtill deficient, for I wanted a Basket or a Wheel-
barrow, a Basket I could not make by any Means, having

no such things as Twigs that would bend to make Wicker
Ware, at least none yet found out; and as to a Wheel-barrow, I fancy'd I could make all but the Wheel, but that I
had no Notion of, neither did I know how to go about it;
besides I had no possible Way to make the Iron Gudge-
ons for the Spindle or Axis of the Wheel to run in, so I
gave it over, and so for carrying away the Earth which I
dug out of the Cave, I made me a Thing like a Hodd,
which the Labourers carry Morter in, when they serve
the Bricklayers.

This was not so difficult to me as the making the Shovel; and yet this, and the Shovel, and the Attempt which
I made in vain, to make a Wheel-Barrow, took me up no
less than four Days, I mean always, excepting my Morning Walk with my Gun, which I seldom fail'd, and very
seldom fail'd also bringing Home something fit to eat.

Nov. 23. My other Work having now stood still, because of my making these Tools; when they were finish'd,
I went on, and working every Day, as my Strength and
Time allow'd, I spent eighteen Days entirely in widening
and deepening my Cave, that it might hold my Goods
commodiously.

Note, During all this Time, I work'd to make this
Room or Cave spacious enough to accommodate me as a
Warehouse or Magazin, a Kitchen, a Dining-room, and
a Cellar; as for my Lodging, I kept to the Tent, except
that some Times in the wet Season of the Year, it rain'd
so hard, that I could not keep my self dry, which caused
me afterwards to cover all my Place within my Pale with
long Poles in the Form of Rafters leaning against the
Rock, and load them with Flaggs and large Leaves of
Trees like a Thatch.

December 10th, I began now to think my Cave or Vault
finished, when on a Sudden, (it seems I had made it too

large) a great Quantity of Earth fell down from the Top
and one Side, so much, that in short it frighted me, and
not without Reason too; for if I had been under it I had
never wanted a Grave-Digger: Upon this Disaſter I had
a great deal of Work to do over again; for I had the loose
Earth to carry out; and which was of more Importance, I
had the Seiling to prop up, so that I might be sure no
more would come down.

Dec. 11. This Day I went to Work with it accordingly, and got two Shores or Poſts pitch'd upright to the
Top, with two Pieces of Boards a-cross over each Poſt,
this I finish'd the next Day; and setting more Poſts up
with Boards, in about a week more I had the Roof secur'd
and the Poſts ſtanding in Rows, serv'd me for Partitions
to part of my House.

Dec. 17. From this Day to the Twentieth I plac'd
Shelves, and knock'd up Nails on the Poſts to hang every
Thing up that could be hung up, and now I began to be
in some Order within Doors.

Dec. 20. Now I carry'd every Thing into the Cave, and
began to furnish my House, and set up some Pieces of
Boards, like a Dresser, to order my Viƈtuals upon, but
Boards began to be very scarce with me; also I made me
another Table.

Dec. 24. Much Rain all Night and all Day, no ſtirring
out.

Dec. 25. Rain all Day.

Dec. 26. No Rain, and the Earth much cooler than before, and pleasanter.

Dec. 27. Kill'd a young Goat, and lam'd another so as
that I catch'd it, and led it Home in a String; when I had
it Home, I bound and splinter'd up its Leg which was
broke, *N. B.* I took such Care of it, that it liv'd, and the
Leg grew well, and as ſtrong as ever; but by my nursing

it so long it grew tame, and fed upon the little Green at
my Door, and would not go away: This was the firſt Time
that I entertain'd a Thought of breeding up some tame
Creatures, that I might have Food when my Powder and
Shot was all spent.

Dec. 28, 29, 30. Great Heats and no Breeze; so that
there was no Stirring abroad, except in the Evening for
Food; this Time I spent in putting all my Things in
Order within Doors.

January 1. Very hot ſtill, but I went abroad early and
late with my Gun, and lay ſtill in the Middle of the Day;
this Evening going farther into the Valleys which lay towards the Center of the Island, I found there was plenty
of Goats, tho' exceeding shy and hard to come at, however I resolv'd to try if I could not bring my Dog to hunt
them down.

Jan. 2. Accordingly, the next Day, I went out with my
Dog, and set him upon the Goats; but I was miſtaken,for
they all fac'd about upon the Dog, and he knew his Danger too well, for he would not come near them.

Jan. 3. I began my Fence or Wall; which being ſtill
jealous of my being attack'd by some Body, I resolv'd to
make very thick and ſtrong.

> **N. B.** *This Wall being describ'd before, I purposely
> omit what was said in the Journal; it is sufficient
> to observe, that I was no less Time than from the
> 3d of* January *to the* 14th *of* April, *working,fin-
> ishing, and perfecting this Wall, tho' it was no
> more than about* 24 *Yards in Length, being a half
> Circle from one Place in the Rock to another Place
> about eight Yards from it, the Door of the Cave be-
> ing in the Center behind it.*

All this Time I work'd very hard, the Rains hindering me many Days, nay sometimes Weeks together; but I thought I should never be perfectly secure 'till this Wall was finish'd; and it is scarce credible what inexpressible Labour every Thing was done with, especially the bringing Piles out of the Woods, and driving them into the Ground, for I made them much bigger than I need to have done.

When this Wall was finished, and the Out-side double fenc'd with a Turf-Wall rais'd up close to it, I perswaded my self, that if any People were to come on Shore there, they would not perceive any Thing like a Habitation; and it was very well I did so, as may be observ'd hereafter upon a very remarkable Occasion.

During this Time, I made my Rounds in the Woods for Game every Day when the Rain admitted me, and made frequent Discoveries in these Walks of something or other to my Advantage; particularly I found a Kind of wild Pidgeons, who built not as Wood Pidgeons in a Tree, but rather as House Pidgeons, in the Holes of the Rocks; and taking some young ones, I endeavoured to breed them up tame, and did so; but when they grew older they flew all away, which perhaps was at first for Want of feeding them, for I had nothing to give them; however I frequently found their nests, and got their young ones, which were very good Meat.

And now, in the managing my houshold Affairs, I found my self wanting in many Things, which I thought at first it was impossible for me to make, as indeed as to some of them it was; *for Instance,* I could never make a Cask to be hooped, I had a small Runlet or two, *as I observed before,* but I cou'd never arrive to the Capacity of making one by them, tho' I spent many Weeks about it;

I could neither put in the Heads, or joint the Staves so
true to one another, as to make them hold Water, so I
gave that also over.

In the next Place, I was at a great Loss for Candle; so
that as soon as ever it was dark, which was generally by
Seven-a-Clock, I was oblig'd to go to Bed: I remembred
the Lamp of Bees-wax with which I made Candles in my
African Adventure, but I had none of that now; the only
Remedy I had was, that when I had kill'd a Goat, I sav'd
the Tallow, and with a little Dish made of Clay, which I
bak'd in the Sun, to which I added a Wick of some Oak-
um, I made me a Lamp; and this gave me Light, tho' not
a clear steady Light like a Candle; in the Middle of all
my Labours it happen'd, that rummaging my Things, I
found a little Bag, which, as I hinted before, had been
fill'd with Corn for the feeding of Poultry, not for this
Voyage, but before, as I suppose, when the Ship came
from *Lisbon*, what little Remainder of Corn had been in
the Bag, was all devour'd with the Rats, and I saw nothing in the Bag but Husks and Dust; and being willing
to have the Bag for some other Use, I think it was to put
Powder in, when I divided it for Fear of the Lightning,
or some such Use, I shook the Husks of Corn out of it on
one Side of my Fortification under the Rock.

It was a little before the great Rains, just now mention'd, that I threw this Stuff away, taking no Notice of
any Thing, and not so much as remembering that I had
thrown any Thing there; when about a Month after, or
thereabout, I saw some few Stalks of something green,
shooting out of the Ground, which I fancy'd might be
some Plant I had not seen, but I was surpriz'd and perfectly astonish'd, when, after a little longer Time, I saw
about ten or twelve Ears come out, which were perfect

green Barley of the same Kind as our *European*, nay, as
our *English* Barley.

It is impossible to express the Astonishment and Confusion of my Thoughts on this Occasion; I had hitherto
acted upon no religious Foundation at all, indeed I had
very few Notions of Religion in my Head, or had entertain'd any Sense of any Thing that had befallen me, otherwise than as a Chance, or, as we lightly say, what pleases
God; without so much as enquiring into the End of Providence in these Things, or his Order in governing
Events in the World: But after I saw Barley grow there,
in a Climate which I know was not proper for Corn, and
especially that I knew not how it came there, it startl'd me
strangely, and I began to suggest, that God had miraculously caus'd this Grain to grow without any Help of
Seed sown, and that it was so directed purely for my Sustenance, on that wild miserable Place.

This touch'd my Heart a little, and brought Tears out
of my Eyes, and I began to bless my self, that such a Pro-
digy of Nature should happen upon my Account; and
this was the more strange to me, because I saw near it still
all along by the Side of the Rock, some other straggling
Stalks, which prov'd to be Stalks of Ryce, and which I
knew, because I had seen it grow in *Africa* when I was
ashore there.

I not only thought these the pure Productions of Providence for my Support, but not doubting, but that there
was more in the Place, I went all over that Part of the Island, where I had been before, peering in every Corner,
and under every Rock, to see for more of it, but I could
not find any; at last it occur'd to my Thoughts, that I had
shook a Bag of Chickens Meat out in that Place, and then
the Wonder began to cease; and I must confess, my re-

ligious Thankfulness to God's Providence began to abate
too upon the Discovering that all this was nothing but
what was common; tho' I ought to have been as thankful
for so ſtrange and unforseen Providence, as if it had been
miraculous; for it was really the Work of Providence as
to me, that should order or appoint, that 10 or 12 Grains
of Corn should remain unspoil'd, (when the Rats had deſtroy'd all the reſt,) as if it had been dropt from Heaven;
as also, that I should throw it out in that particular Place,
where it being in the Shade of a high Rock, it sprang up
immediately; whereas, if I had thrown it anywhere else,
at that Time, it had been burnt up and deſtroy'd.

I carefully sav'd the Ears of this Corn you may be sure
in their Season, which was about the End of *June*; and
laying up every Corn, I resolv'd to sow them all again,
hoping in Time to have some Quantity sufficient to supply me with Bread; But it was not till the 4th Year that I
could allow my self the leaſt Grain of this Corn to eat, and
even then but sparingly, as I shall say afterwards in its
Order; for I loſt all that I sow'd the firſt Season, by not
observing the proper Time; for I sow'd it juſt before the
dry Season, so that it never came up at all, at leaſt, not as
it would ha' done: Of which in its Place.

Besides this Barley, there was, as above, 20 or 30 Stalks
of Ryce, which I preserv'd with the same Care, and whose
Use was of the same Kind or to the same Purpose, (*viz.*)
to make me Bread, or rather Food; for I found Ways to
cook it up without baking, tho' I did that also after some
Time. But to return to my Journal.

I work'd excessive hard these three or four Months to
get my Wall done; and the 14th of *April* I closed it up,
contriving to go into it, not by a Door, but over the Wall

by a Ladder, that there might be no Sign in the Out-side of my Habitation.

April 16. I finish'd the Ladder, so I went up with the Ladder to the Top, and then pull'd it up after me, and let it down in the In-side: This was a compleat Enclosure to me; for within I had Room enough, and nothing could come at me from without, unless it could first mount my Wall.

The very next Day after this Wall was finish'd, I had almost had all my Labour overthrown at once, and my self kill'd, the Case was thus, As I was busy in the Inside of it, behind my Tent, just in the Entrance into my Cave, I was terribly frighted with a most dreadful surprising Thing indeed; for all on a sudden I found the Earth come crumbling down from the Roof of my Cave, and from the Edge of the Hill over my Head, and two of the Posts I had set up in the Cave crack'd in a frightful Manner; I was heartily scar'd, but thought nothing of what was really the Cause, only thinking that the Top of my Cave was falling in, as some of it had done before; and for Fear I shou'd be bury'd in it, I ran foreward to my Ladder, and not thinking my self safe there neither, I got over my Wall for Fear of the Pieces of the Hill which I expected might roll down upon me: I was no sooner stepp'd down upon the firm Ground, but I plainly saw it was a terrible Earthquake, for the Ground I stood on shook three Times at about eight Minutes Distance, with three such Shocks as would have overturn'd the strongest Building that could be suppos'd to have stood on the Earth, and a great Piece of the Top of a Rock, which stood about half a Mile from me next the Sea, fell down with such a terrible Noise as I never heard in all my Life: I perceiv'd also, the very

Sea was put into violent Motion by it; and I believe the
Shocks were stronger under the Water than on the Island.

I was so amaz'd with the Thing it self, having never
felt the like, or discours'd with any one that had, that I
was like one dead or stupify'd; and the Motion of the
Earth made my Stomach sick like one that was toss'd at
Sea; but the Noise of the falling of the Rock awak'd me
as it were, and rousing me from the stupify'd Condition I
was in, fill'd me with Horror, and I thought of nothing
then but the Hill falling upon my Tent and all my houshold Goods, and burying all at once; and this sunk my
very Soul within me a second Time.

After the third Shock was over, and I felt no more for
some Time, I began to take Courage, and yet I had not
Heart enough to go over my Wall again, for Fear of being buried alive, but sat still upon the Ground, greatly
cast down and disconsolate, not knowing what to do: All
this while I had not the least serious religious Thought,
nothing but the common, *Lord ha' Mercy upon me*; and
when it was over, that went away too.

While I sat this, I found the Air over-cast, and grow
cloudy, as if it would Rain; soon after that the Wind rose
by little and little, so that, in less than half an Hour, it
blew a most dreadful Hurricane: The Sea was all on a
Sudden cover'd over with Foam and Froth, the Shore
was cover'd with the Breach of the Water, the Trees were
torn up by the Roots, and a terrible Storm it was; and
this held about three Hours, and then began to abate,
and in two Hours more it was stark calm, and began to
rain very hard.

All this while I sat upon the Ground very much terrify'd and dejected, when on a sudden it came into my

thoughts, that these Winds and Rain being the Consequences of the Earthquake, the Earthquake it self was
spent and over, and I might venture into my Cave again:
With this Thought my Spirits began to revive, and the
Rain also helping to perswade me, I went in and sat down
in my Tent, but the Rain was so violent, that my Tent
was ready to be beaten down with it, and I was forc'd to
go into my Cave, tho' very much afraid and uneasy for
fear it should fall on my Head.

This violent Rain forc'd me to a new Work, *viz*. To
cut a Hole thro' my new Fortification like a Sink to let the
Water go out, which would else have drown'd my Cave.
After I had been in my Cave some time, and found still no
more Shocks of the Earthquake follow, I began to be
more compos'd; and now to support my Spirits, which
indeed wanted it very much, I went to my little Store and
took a small Sup of Rum, which however I did then and
always very sparingly, knowing I could have no more
when that was gone.

It continu'd raining all that Night, and great Part of
the next Day, so that I could not stir abroad, but my Mind
being more compos'd, I began to think of what I had best
do, concluding that if the Island was subject to these
Earthquakes, there would be no living for me in a Cave,
but I must consider of building me some little Hut in an
open Place which I might surround with a Wall as I had
done here, and so make my self secure from wild Beasts
or Men; but concluded, if I staid where I was, I should
certainly, one time or other, be bury'd alive.

With these Thoughts I resolv'd to remove my Tent
from the Place where it stood, which was just under the
hanging Precipice of the Hill, and which, if it should be
shaken again, would certainly fall upon my Tent: And I

spent the two next Days, being the 19th and 20th of *April*, in contriving where and how to remove my Habitation.

The fear of being swallow'd up alive, made me that I never slept in quiet, and yet the Apprehensions of lying abroad without any Fence was almost equal to it; but still when I look'd about and saw how every thing was put in order, how pleasantly conceal'd I was, and how safe from Danger, it made me very loath to remove.

In the mean time it occur'd to me that it would require a vast deal of time for me to do this, and that I must be contented to run the Venture where I was, till I had form'd a Camp for my self, and had secur'd it so as to remove to it: So with this Resolution I compos'd my self for a time, and resolv'd that I would go to work with all Speed to build me a Wall with Piles and Cables, &c. in a Circle as before, and set my Tent up in it when it was finish'd, but that I would venture to stay where I was till it was finish'd and fit to remove to. This was the 21st.

April 22. The next Morning I began to consider of Means to put this Resolve in Execution, but I was at a great loss about my Tools; I had three large Axes and abundance of Hatchets, (for we carried the Hatchets for Traffick with the *Indians*) but with much chopping and cutting knotty hard Wood, they were all full of Notches and dull, and tho' I had a Grindstone, I could not turn it and grind my Tools too, this cost me as much Thought as a Statesman would have bestow'd upon a grand Point of Politicks, or a Judge upon the Life and Death of a Man. At length I contriv'd a Wheel with a String, to turn it with my Foot, that I might have both my Hands at Liberty: *Note*, I had never seen any such thing in *England*, or at least not to take Notice how it was done, tho' since I

have observ'd it is very common there: besides that, my
Grindstone was very large and heavy. This Machine cost
me a full Weeks Work to bring it to Perfection.

April 28, 29. These two whole Days I took up in grind-
ing my Tools, my Machine for turning my Grindstone
performing very well.

April 30. Having perceiv'd my Bread had been low a
great while, now I took a Survey of it, and reduc'd my self
to one Bisket-cake a Day, which made my Heart very
heavy.

May 1. In the Morning looking towards the Sea-side,
the Tide being low, I saw something lye on the Shore
bigger than ordinary, and it look'd like a Cask, when I
came to it, I found a small Barrel, and two or three Pieces
of the Wreck of the Ship, which were driven on Shore by
the late Hurricane, and looking towards the Wreck itself
I thought it seem'd to lye higher out of the Water than it
us'd to do; I examin'd the Barrel which was driven on
Shore, and soon found it was a Barrel of Gunpowder, but
it had taken Water, and the Powder was cak'd as hard as
a Stone, however I roll'd it farther on Shore for the present, and went on upon the Sands as near as I could to the
Wreck of the Ship to look for more.

When I came down to the Ship I found it strangely remov'd, The Fore-castle which lay before bury'd in Sand,
was heav'd up at least Six Foot, and the Stern which was
broke to Pieces and parted from the rest by the Force of
the Sea soon after I had left rummaging her, was toss'd,
as it were, up, and cast on one Side, and the Sand was
thrown so high on that Side next her Stern, that whereas
there was a great Place of Water before, so that I could
not come within a Quarter of a Mile of the Wreck without swimming, I could now walk quite up to her when

the Tide was out; I was surpris'd with this at firſt, but soon concluded it muſt be done by the Earthquake, and as by this Violence the Ship was more broken open than formerly, so many Things came daily on Shore, which the Sea had loosen'd, and which the Winds and Water rolled by Degrees to the Land .

This wholly diverted my Thoughts from the Design of removing my Habitation; and I busied my self mightily that Day especially, in searching whether I could make any Way into the Ship, but I found nothing was to be expeĉted of that Kind, for that all the In-side of the Ship was choak'd up with Sand: Hawever, as I had learn'd not to despair of any Thing, I resolv'd to pull every Thing to Pieces that I could of the Ship, concluding, that every Thing I could get from her would be of some Use or other to me.

May 3. I began with my Saw, and cut a Piece of a Beam thro', which I thought held some of the upper Part or Quarter-Deck together, and when I had cut it thro', I clear'd away the Sand as well as I could from the Side which lay higheſt; but the Tide coming in, I was oblig'd to give over for that Time.

May 4. I went a fishing, but caught not one Fish that I durſt eat of, till I was weary of my Sport, when juſt going to leave off, I caught a young Dolphin. I had made me a long Line of some Rope Yarn, but I had no Hooks, yet I frequently caught Fish enough, as much as I car'd to eat; all which I dry'd in the Sun, and eat them dry.

May 5. Work'd on the Wreck, cut another Beam asunder, and brought three great Fir Planks off from the Decks, which I ty'd together, and made swim on Shore when the Tide of Flood came on.

May 6. Work'd on the Wreck, got several Iron Bolts

out of her, and other Pieces of Iron Work, work'd very hard, and came Home very much tyr'd, and had Thoughts of giving it over.

May 7. Went to the Wreck again, but with an Intent not to work, but found the Weight of the Wreck had broke itself down, the Beams being cut, that several Pieces of the Ship seem'd to lie loose, and the In-side of the Hold lay so open, that I could see into it, but almost full of Water and Sand.

May 8. Went to the Wreck, and carry'd an Iron Crow to wrench up the Deck, which lay now quite clear of the Water or Sand; I wrench'd open two Planks, and brought them on Shore also with the Tide; I left the Iron Crow in the Wreck for next Day.

May 9. Went to the Wreck, and with the Crow made Way into the Body of the Wreck, and felt several Casks, and loosen'd them with the Crow, but could not break them up; I felt also the Roll of *English* Lead, and could stir it, but it was too heavy to remove.

May 10, 11, 12, 13, 14. Went every Day to the Wreck, and got a great deal of Pieces of Timber, and Boards, or Plank, and 2 or 300 Weight of Iron.

May 15. I carry'd two Hatchets to try if I could not cut a Piece off of the Roll of Lead, by placing the Edge of one Hatchet, and driving it with the other; but as it lay about a Foot and a half in the Water, I could not make any Blow to drive the Hatchet.

May 16. It had blow'd hard in the Night, and the Wreck appear'd more broken by the Force of the Water but I stay'd so long in the Woods to get Pidgeons for Food, that the Tide prevented me going to the Wreck that Day.

May 17. I saw some Pieces of the Wreck blown on

Shore, at a great Diſtance, near two Miles off me, but resolv'd to see what they were, and found it was a Piece of
the Head, but too heavy for me to bring away.

May 24. Every Day to this Day I work'd on theWreck
and with hard Labour I loosen'd some Things so much
with the Crow, that the firſt blowing Tide several Casks
floated out, and two of the Seamen's Cheſts; but the
Wind blowing from the Shore, nothing came to Land
that Day, but Pieces of Timber, and a Hogshead which
had some *Brazil* Pork in it, but the Salt-water and the
Sand had spoil'd it.

I continu'd this Work every Day to the 15th of *June*,
except the Time necessary to get Food, which I always
appointed, during this Part of my Employment, to be
when the Tide was up, that I might be ready when it was
ebb'd out, and by this Time I had gotten Timber, and
Plank, and Iron-Work enough, to have builded a good
Boat, if I had known how; and also, I got at severalTimes
and in several Pieces, near 100 Weight of the Sheat-
Lead.

June 16. Going down to the Sea-side, I found a large
Tortoise or Turtle; this was the firſt I had seen, which it
seems was only my Misfortune, not any Defeƌt of the
Place, or Scarcity; for had I happen'd to be on the other
Side of the Island, I might have had Hundreds of them
every Day, as I found afterwards; but perhaps had paid
dear enough for them.

June 17. I spent in cooking the Turtle; I found in her
threescore Eggs; and her Flesh was to me at that Time
the moſt savoury and pleasant that ever I taſted in my
Life, having had no Flesh, but of Goats and Fowls, since
I landed in this horrid Place.

June 18. Rain'd all Day, and I ſtay'd within. I thought

at this Time the Rain felt Cold, and I was something chilly, which I knew was not usual in that Latitude.

June 19. Very ill, and shivering, as if the Weather had been cold.

June 20. No rest all Night, violent Pains in my Head, and feverish.

June 21. Very ill, frighted almost to Death with the Apprehensions of my sad Condition, to be sick, and no Help: pray'd to G O D for the first Time since the Storm off of *Hull*, but scarce knew what I said, or why; my Thoughts being all confused.

June 22. A little better, but under dreadful Apprehensions of Sickness.

June 23. Very bad again, cold shivering, and then a violent Head-ach.

June 24. Much better.

June 25. An Ague very violent; the Fit held me seven Hours, cold Fit and hot, with faint Sweats after it.

June 26. Better; and having no Victuals to eat, took my Gun, but found my self very weak; however I kill'd a She-Goat, and with much Difficulty got it Home, and broil'd some of it, and eat; I wou'd fain have stew'd it, and made some Broath, but had no Pot.

June 27. The Ague again so violent, that I lay a-Bed all Day, and neither eat or drank. I was ready to perish for Thirst, but so weak, I had not Strength to stand up, or to get my self any Water to drink: Pray'd to God again, but was light-headed, and when I was not, I was so ignorant, that I knew not what to say; only I lay and cry'd, *Lord look upon me, Lord pity me, Lord have Mercy upon me:* I suppose I did nothing else for two or three Hours, till the Fit wearing off, I fell asleep, and did not wake till far in the Night; when I wak'd, I found my self much refresh'd, but weak, and exceeding thirsty: However, as I had no Water in my whole Habitation, I was forc'd to lie till Morning, and went to sleep again: In this second Sleep, I had this terrible Dream.

I thought, that I was sitting on the Ground on the Outside of my Wall, where I sat when the Storm blew after the Earthquake, and that I saw a Man descend from a great black Cloud, in a bright Flame of Fire, and light upon the Ground: He was all over as bright as a Flame, so that I could but juſt bear to look towards him; his Countenance was moſt inexpressibly dreadful, impossible for Words to describe; when he ſtepp'd upon the Ground with his Feet, I thought the Earth trembl'd, juſt as it had done before in the Earthquake, and all the Air look'd, to my Apprehension, as if it had been fill'd with Flashes of Fire.

He was no sooner landed upon the Earth, but he moved forward towards me, with a long Spear or Weapon in his Hand, to kill me; and when he came to a rising Ground, at some Diſtance, he spoke to me, or I heard a Voice so terrible, that it is impossible to express the Terror of it; all that I can say I underſtood, was this, *Seeing all these Things have not brought thee to Repentance, now thou shalt die*: At which Words, I thought he lifted up the Spear that was in his Hand, to kill me.

No one, that shall ever read this Account, will expeƈt that I should be able to describe the Horrors of my Soul at this terrible Vision, I mean, that even while it was a Dream, I even dreamed of those Horrors; nor is it any more possible to describe the Impression that remain'd upon my Mind when I awak'd and found it was but a Dream.

I had alas! no divine Knowledge; what I had received

by the good Instruction of my Father was then worn out
by an uninterrupted Series, for 8 Years, of Seafaring
Wickedness, and a constant Conversation with nothing
but such as were like my self, wicked and prophane to the
last Degree: I do not remember that I had in all thatTime
one Thought that so much as tended either to looking
upwards toward God, or inwards towards a Reflection
upon my own Ways: But a certain Stupidity of Soul,
without Desire of Good, or Conscience of Evil, had entirely overwhelm'd me, and I was all that the most hardned, unthinking, wicked Creature among our common
Sailors, can be supposed to be, not having the least Sense,
either of the Fear of God in Danger, or of Thankfulness
to God in Deliverances.

In the relating what is already past of my Story, this
will be the more easily believ'd, when I shall add, that
thro' all the Variety of Miseries that had to this Day befallen me, I never had so much as one Thought of it being
the Hand of God, or that it was a just Punishment for my
Sin; my rebellious Behaviour against my Father, or my
present Sins which were great; or so much as a Punishment for the general Course of my wicked Life. When I
was on the desperate Expedition on the desart Shores of
Africa, I never had so much as one Thought of what would
become of me; or one Wish to God to direct me whither I
should go, or to keep me from the Danger which apparently surrounded me, as well from voracious Creatures
as cruel Savages: But I was meerly thoughtless of a God,
or a Providence; acted like a meer Brute from the Principles of Nature, and by the Dictates of common Sense only, and indeed hardly that.

When I was deliver'd and taken up at Sea by the *Portugal* Captain, well us'd, and dealt justly and honourably

with, as well as charitably, I had not the least Thankfulness on my Thoughts: When again I was shipwreck'd,
ruin'd, and in Danger of drowning on this Island, I was
as far from Remorse, or looking on it as a Judgment; I only said to my self often, that I was *an unfortunate Dog*, and
born to be always miserable.

It is true, when I got on Shore first here, and found all
my Ship's Crew drown'd, and my self spar'd, I was surpriz'd with a Kind of Extasie, and some Transports of
Soul, which, had the Grace of God assisted, might have
come up to true Thankfulness; but it ended where it begun, in a meer common Flight of Joy, or as I may say, *being glad I was alive*, without the least Reflection upon the
distinguishing Goodness of the Hand which had preserv'd me, and had singled me out to be preserv'd, when
all the rest were destroy'd; or an Enquiry why Providence
had been thus merciful to me; even just the same common
Sort of Joy which Seamen generally have after they are
got safe ashore from a Shipwreck, which they drown all
in the next Bowl of Punch, and forget almost as soon as it
is over, and all the rest of my Life was like it.

Even when I was afterwards, on due Consideration,
made sensible of my Condition, how I was cast on this
dreadful Place, out of the Reach of humane Kind, out of
all Hope of Relief, or Prospect of Redemption, as soon as
I saw but a Prospect of living, and that I should not starve
and perish for Hunger, all the Sense of my Affliction wore
off, and I begun to be very easy, apply'd my self to the
Works proper for my Preservation and Supply, and was
far enough from being afflicted at my Condition, as a
Judgment from Heaven, or as the Hand of God against
me; these were Thoughts which very seldom enter'd into my Head.

The growing up of the Corn, as is hinted in my Journal, had at firſt some little Influence upon me, and began to affeƈt me with Seriousness, as long as I thought it had something miraculous in it; but as soon as ever that Part of the Thought was remov'd, all the Impression which was rais'd from it, wore off also, as I have noted already.

Even the Earthquake, tho' nothing could be more terrible in its Nature, or more immediately direƈting to the Invisible Power which alone direƈts such Things, yet no sooner was the firſt Fright over, but the Impression it had made went off also. I had no more Sense of God or his Judgments, much less of the present Affliƈtion of my Circumſtances being from his Hand, than if I had been in the moſt prosperous Condition of Life.

But now when I began to be sick, and a leisurely View of the Miseries of Death came to place itself before me; when my Spirits began to sink under the Burthen of a ſtrong Diſtemper, and Nature was exhauſted with the Violence of the Feaver; Conscience that had slept so long, begun to awake, and I began to reproach my self with my paſt Life, in which I had so evidently, by uncommon Wickedness, provok'd the Juſtice of God to lay me under uncommon Strokes, and to deal with me in so vindiƈtive a Manner.

These Refleƈtions oppress'd me for the second or third Day of my Diſtemper, and in the Violence, as well of the Feaver, as of the dreadful Reproaches of my Conscience, extorted some Words from me, like praying to God, tho' I cannot say they were either a Prayer attended with Desires or with Hopes; it was rather the Voice of meer Fright and Diſtress; my Thoughts were confus'd, the Convictions great upon my Mind, and the Horror of dying in such a miserable Condition rais'd Vapours into my Head

with the meer Apprehensions; and in these Hurries of
my Soul, I know not what my Tongue might express:
but it was rather Exclamation, such as, Lord! what a
miserable Creature am I? If I should be sick, I shall certainly die for Want of Help, and what will become of me!
Then the Tears burst out of my Eyes, and I could say no
more for a good while.

In this Interval, the good Advice of my Father came
to my Mind, and presently his Prediction which I mention'd at the Beginning of this Story, *viz. That if I did
take this foolish Step, God would not bless me, and I would
have Leisure hereafter to reflect upon having neglected his
Counsel, when there might be none to assist in my Recovery.*
Now, said I aloud, My dear Father's Words are come to
pass: God's Justice has overtaken me, and I have none to
help or hear me: I rejected the Voice of Providence,
which had mercifully put me in a Posture or Station of
Life, wherein I might have been happy and easy; but I
would neither see it my self, or learn to know the Blessing
of it from my Parents; I left them to mourn over my Folly, and now I am left to mourn under the Consequences of
it; I refus'd their Help and Assistance who wou'd have
lifted me into the World, and wou'd have made every
Thing easy to me, and now I have Difficulties to struggle
with, too great even for Nature itself to support, and no
Assistance, no Help, no Comfort, no Advice; then I
cry'd out, *Lord be my Help, for I am in great Distress.*

This was the first Prayer, if I may call it so, that I had
made for many Years: But I return to my Journal.

June 28. Having been somewhat refresh'd with the
Sleep I had had, and the Fit being entirely off, I got up;
and tho' the Fright and Terror of my Dream was very

great, yet I consider'd, that the Fit of the Ague wou'd return again the next Day, and now was my Time to get
something to refresh and support my self when I should
be ill; and the firſt thing I did, I fill'd a large square Case
Bottle with Water, and set it upon my Table, in Reach
of my Bed; and to take off the chill or aguish Dispositi-
tion of the Water, I put about a Quarter of a Pint of Rum
into it, and mix'd them together; then I got me a Piece of
the Goat's Flesh, and broil'd it on the Coals, but could
eat very little; I walk'd about, but was very weak, and
withal very sad and heavy-hearted in the Sense of my
miserable Condition; dreading the Return of my Distemper the next Day; at Night I made my Supper of three
of the Turtle's Eggs, which I roaſted in the Ashes, and
eat, as we call it, in the Shell; and this was the firſt Bit of
Meat I had ever ask'd God's Blessing to, even as I cou'd
remember, in my whole Life.

After I had eaten, I try'd to walk, but found my self so
weak, that I cou'd hardly carry the Gun, (for I never went
out without that) so I went but a little Way, and sat down
upon the Ground, looking out upon the Sea, which was
juſt before me, and very calm and smooth: As I sat here,
some such Thoughts as these occurred to me.

What is this Earth and Sea of which I have seen so
much, whence is it produc'd, and what am I, and all the
other Creatures, wild and tame, humane and brutal,
whence are we?

Sure we are all made by some secret Power, who form'd
the Earth and Sea, the Air and Sky; and who is that?

Then it follow'd moſt naturally, It is God that has
made it all: Well, but then it came on ſtrangely, if God
has made all these Things, He guides and governs them

all, and all Things that concern them; for the Power that could make all Things, must certainly have Power to guide and direct them.

If so, nothing can happen in the great Circuit of his Works, either without his Knowledge or Appointment.

And if nothing happens without his Knowledge, he knows that I am here, and am in this dreadful Condition; and if nothing happens without his Appointment, he has appointed all this to befal me.

Nothing occurr'd to my Thought to contradict any of these Conclusions; and therefore it rested upon me with the greater Force, that it must needs be, that God had appointed all this to befal me; that I was brought to this miserable Circumstance by his Direction, he having the sole Power, not of me only, but of every Thing that happen'd in the World. Immediately it follow'd,

Why has God done this to me? What have I done to be thus us'd?

My Conscience presently check'd me in that Enquiry, as if I had blasphem'd, and methought it spoke to me like a Voice; W R E T C H ! *dost thou ask what thou hast done!* look back upon a dreadful mis-spent Life, and ask thy self *what thou hast not done?* ask, Why is it *that thou wert not long ago destroy'd?* Why *wert thou not drown'd in* Yarmouth Roads? *Kill'd in the Fight when the Ship was taken by* the Sallee man of War? *Devour'd by the wild Beasts on the* Coast of Africa? Or, *Drown'd H E R E , when all the Crew perish'd but thy self?* Dost thou ask, *What have I done?*

I was struck dumb with these Reflections, as one astonish'd, and had not a Word to say, no not to answer to my self, but rose up pensive and sad, walk'd back to my Retreat, and went up over my Wall, as if I had been going to

Bed, but my Thoughts were sadly diſturb'd, and I had no
Inclination to Sleep; so I sat down in my Chair, and light-
ed my Lamp, for it began to be dark: Now as the Apprehension of the Return of my Diſtemper terrify'd me very
much, it occurr'd to my Thought, that the *Brasilians* take
no Physick but their Tobacco, for almoſt all Diſtempers;
and I had a Piece of a Roll of Tobacco in one of theCheſts
which was quite cur'd, and some also that was green and
not quite cur'd.

I went, direĉted by Heaven no doubt; for in this
Cheſt I found a Cure, both for Soul and Body, I open'd
the Cheſt, and found what I look'd for, *viz.* the Tobacco;
and as the few Books, I had sav'd, lay there too, I took out
one of the Bibles which I mention'd before, and which to
this Time I had not found Leisure, or so much as Inclination to look into; I say, I took it out, and brought both
that and the Tobacco with me to the Table.

What Use to make of the Tobacco, I knew not, as to
my Diſtemper, or whether it was good for it or no; but I
try'd several Experiments with it, as if I was resolv'd it
should hit one Way or other: I firſt took a Piece of a Leaf,
and chew'd it in my Mouth, which indeed at firſt almoſt
ſtupify'd my Brain, the Tobacco being green and ſtrong,
and that I had not been much us'd to it: then I took some
and ſteeped it an Hour or two in some Rum, and resolv'd
to take a Dose of it when I lay down; and laſtly, I burnt
some upon a Pan of Coals, and held my Nose close over
the Smoke of it as long as I could bear it, as well for the
Heat as almoſt for Suffocation.

In the Interval of this Operation, I took up the Bible
and began to read, but my Head was too much diſturb'd
with the Tobacco to bear reading, at leaſt that Time; only
having opened the Book casually, the firſt Words that

occurr'd to me were these, *Call on me in the Day of Trouble, and I will deliver, and thou shalt glorify me.*

The Words were very apt to my Case, and made some Impression upon my Thoughts at the Time of reading them, tho' not so much as they did afterwards; for as for being deliver'd, the Word had no Sound, *as I may say,* to me; the Thing was so remote, so impossible in my Apprehension of Things, that I began to say as the Children of *Israel* did, when they were promis'd Flesh to eat, *Can God spread a Table in the Wilderness*; so I began to say, Can God himself deliver me from this Place? and as it was not for many Years that any Hope appear'd, this prevail'd very often upon my Thoughts: But however, the Words made a great Impression upon me, and I mused upon them very often. It grew now late, and the Tobacco had, as I said, doz'd my Head so much, that I inclin'd to sleep; so I left my Lamp burning in the Cave, least I should want any Thing in the Night, and went to Bed; but before I lay down, I did what I never had done in all my Life, I kneel'd down and pray'd to God to fulfil the Promise to me, that if I call'd upon him in the Day of Trouble, he would deliver me; after my broken and imperfect Prayer was over, I drunk the Rum in which I had steep'd the Tobacco, which was so strong and rank of the Tobacco, that indeed I could scarce get it down; immediately upon this I went to Bed, I found presently it flew up in my Head violently, but I fell into a sound Sleep, and wak'd no more 'till by the Sun it must necessarily be near Three a-Clock in the Afternoon the next Day; nay, to this Hour, I'm partly of the Opinion, that I slept all the next Day and Night, and 'till almost Three that Day after; for otherwise I knew not how I should lose a Day out of my Reckoning in the Days of the Week, as it appear'd

some Years after I had done: for if I had loſt it by crossing and re-crossing the Line, I should have loſt more
than one Day: But certainly I loſt a Day in my Accompt,
and never knew which Way.

Be that however one Way or th' other, when I awak'd
I found my self exceedingly refresh'd, and my Spirits
lively and chearful; when I got up, I was ſtronger than I
was the Day before, and my Stomach better, for I was
hungry; and in short, I had no Fit the next Day, but continu'd much alter'd for the better; this was the 29th.

The 30th was my well Day of Course, and I went
abroad with my Gun, but did not care to travel too far, I
kill'd a Sea Fowl or two, something like a brand Goose,
and brought them Home, but was not very forward to eat
them; so I ate some more of the Turtle's Eggs, which
were very good: This Evening I renew'd the Medicine
which I had suppos'd did me good the Day before, *viz.*
the Tobacco ſteep'd in Rum, only I did not take so much
as before, nor did I chew any of the Leaf, or hold my
Head over the Smoke,; however I was not so well the
next Day, which was the firſt of *July*, as I hop'd I shou'd
have been; for I had a little Spice of the cold Fit, but it
was not much.

July 2. I renew'd the Medicine all the three Ways, and
doz'd my self with it as at firſt; and doubled the Quantity
which I drank.

3. I miss'd the Fit for good and all, tho' I did not recover my full Strength for some Weeks after; while I was
thus gathering Strength, my Thoughts run exceedingly
upon this Scripture, *I will deliver thee*, and the Impossi-
bility of my Deliverance lay much upon my Mind in
Barr of my ever expecting it: But as I was discouraging
my self with such Thoughts, it occurr'd to my Mind, that

I pored so much upon my Deliverance from the main Affliction, that I disregarded the Deliverance I had receiv'd;
and I was, as it were, made to ask my self such Questions
as these, *viz.* Have I not been deliver'd, and wonderfully
too, from Sickness? from the most distress'd Condition
that could be, and that was so frightful to me, and what
Notice I had taken of it: Had I done my Part, *God had deliver'd me, but I had not glorify'd him*; that is to say, I had
not own'd and been thankful for that as a Deliverance,
and how cou'd I expect greater Deliverance?

This touch'd my Heart very much, and immediately I
kneel'd down and gave God Thanks aloud, for my Recovery from my Sickness.

July 4. In the Morning I took the Bible, and beginning
at the New Testament, I began seriously to read it, and
impos'd upon my self to read a while every Morning and
every Night, not tying my self to the Number of Chap-
ters, but as long as my Thoughts shou'd engage me: It
was not long after I set seriously to this Work, but I found
my Heart more deeply and sincerely affected with the
Wickedness of my past Life: The Impression of my
Dream reviv'd, and the Words, *All these Things have not
brought thee to Repentance*, ran seriously in my Thought: I
was earnestly begging of God to give me Repentance,
when it happen'd providentially the very Day that reading the Scriture, I came to these Words, *He is exalted a
Prince and a Saviour, to give Repentance, and to give Re-
mission*: I threw down the Book, and with my Heart as
well as my Hands lifted up to Heaven, in a Kind of Ex-
tasy of Joy, I cry'd out aloud, *Jesus, thou Son of* David,
Jesus, thou exalted Prince and Saviour, give me Repentance!
This was the first time That I could say, in the true
Sense of the Words, that I pray'd in all my Life; for now

I pray'd with a Sense of my Condition, and with a true Scripture View of Hope founded on the Encouragement of the Word of God; and from this Time, I may say, I began to have Hope that God would hear me.

Now I began to construe the Words mentioned above, *Call on me, and I will deliver you,* in a different Sense from what I had ever done before; for then I had no Notion of any thing being call'd Deliverance, but my being deliver'd from the Captivity I was in; for tho' I was indeed at large in the Place, yet the Island was certainly a Prison to me, and that in the worst Sense in the World; but now I learn'd to take it in another Sense: Now I look'd back upon my past Life with such Horrour, and my Sins appear'd so dreadful, that my Soul sought nothing of God, but Deliverance from the Load of Guilt that bore down all my Comfort: As for my solitary Life it was nothing; I did not so much as pray to be deliver'd from it, or think of it; It was all of no Consideration in Comparison to this: And I add this Part here, to hint to whoever shall read it, that whenever they come to a true Sense of things, they, will find Deliverance from Sin a much greater Blessing than Deliverance from Affliction.

But leaving this Part, I return to my Journal.

My Condition began now to be, tho' not less miserable as to my Way of living, yet much easier to my Mind; and my Thoughts being directed, by a constant reading the Scripture, and praying to God, to things of a higher Nature: I had a great deal of Comfort within, which till now I knew nothing of; also, as my Health and Strength returned, I bestirr'd my self to furnish my self with every thing that I wanted, and make my Way of living as regular as I could.

From the 4th of *July* to the 14th, I was chiefly employ'd in walking about with my Gun in my Hand, a little and a little, at a Time, as a Man that was gathering up his Strength after a Fit of Sickness: For it is hardly to be imagin'd, how low I was, and to what Weakness I was reduc'd. The Application which I made Use of was perfectly new, and perhaps what had never cur'd an Ague before, neither can I recommend it to any one to practise, by this Experiment; and tho' it did carry off the Fit, yet it rather contributed to weakening me; for I had frequent Convulsions in my Nerves and Limbs for some Time.

I learn'd from it also this in particular, that being abroad in the rainy Season was the most pernicious thing to my Health that could be, especially in those Rains which came attended with Storms and Hurricanes of Wind; for as the Rain which came in the dry Season was always most accompany'd with such Storms, so I found that Rain was much more dangerous than the Rain which fell in *September* and *October*.

I had been now in this unhappy Island above 10 Months, all Possibility of Deliverance from this Condition, seem'd to be entirely taken from me; and I firmly believed, that no humane Shape had ever set Foot upon that Place. Having now secur'd my Habitation, as I thought, fully to my Mind, I had a great Desire to make a more perfect Discovery of the Island, and to see what other Productions I might find, which I yet knew nothing of.

It was the 15th of *July* that I began to take a more particular Survey of the Island it self: I went up the Creek first, where, as I hinted, I brought my Rafts on Shore; I found after I came about two Miles up, that the Tide did not flow any higher, and that it was no more than a little Brook of running Water, and very fresh and good; but this being the dry Season, there was hardly any Water in some Parts of it, at leaſt, not enough to run in any Stream so as it could be perceiv'd.

On the Bank of this Brook I found many pleasant *Savana's*, or Meadows; plain, smooth, and cover'd with Grass; and on the rising Parts of them next to the higher Grounds, where the Water, as it might be supposed, never overflow'd, I found a great deal of Tobacco, green, and growing to a great and very ſtrong Stalk; there were divers other Plants which I had no Notion of, or Underſtanding about, and might perhaps have Vertues of their own, which I could not find out.

I searched for the *Cassava* Root, which the *Indians* in all that Climate make their Bread of, but I could find none. I saw large Plants of Alloes, but did not then underſtand them. I saw several Sugar Canes, but wild, and for want of Cultivation, imperfeꞔt. I contented my self with these Discoveries for this Time, and came back musing with my self what Course I might take to know the Vertue and Goodness of any of the Fruits or Plants which I should discover; but could bring it to no Conclusion; for in short, I had made so little Observation while I was in the *Brasils*, that I knew little of the Plants in the Field, at leaſt very little that might serve me to any Purpose now in my Diſtress.

The next Day, the 16th, I went up the same Way again, and after going something farther than I had gone the Day before, I found the Brook, and the *Savana's* began to cease, and the Country became more woody than before; in this Part I found different Fruits, and particularly I found Mellons upon the Ground in great Abundance, and Grapes upon the Trees; the Vines had spread indeed over the Trees, and the Cluſters of Grapes were juſt now in their Prime, very ripe and rich: This was a surprising Discovery, and I was exceeding glad of them; but I was warn'd by my Experience to eat sparingly of them, remembring, that when I was ashore in *Barbary*, the eating of Grapes kill'd several of our *English* Men who were Slaves there, by throwing them into Fluxes and Feavers: But I found an excellent Use for these Grapes, and that was to cure or dry them in the Sun, and keep them as dry'd Grapes or Raisins are kept, which I thought would be, as indeed they were, as wholesom as agreeable to eat, when no Grapes might be to be had.

I spent all that Evening there, and went not back to my Habitation, which, by the Way was the firſt Night as I might say, I had lain from Home. In the Night I took my firſt Contrivance, and got up into a Tree, where I slept well, and the next Morning proceeded upon my Discovery, travelling near four Miles, as I might judge by the Length of the Valley, keeping ſtill due North, with a Ridge of Hills on the South and North-side of me.

At the End of this March I came to an Opening, where the Country seem'd to descend to the Weſt, and a little Spring of fresh Water which issued out of the Side of the Hill by me, run the other Way, that is due Eaſt; and the Country appear'd so fresh, so green, so flourishing, every thing being in a conſtant Verdure, or Flourish of *Spring*, that it looked like a planted Garden.

I descended a little on the Side of that delicious Vale, surveying it with a secret Kind of Pleasure, (tho' mixt with my other afflicting Thoughts) to think that this was all my own, that I was King and Lord of all this Country indefeasibly, and had a Right of Possession; and if I could convey it, I might have it in Inheritance, as compleatly as any Lord of a Mannor in *England*. I saw here

Abundance of Cocoa Trees, Orange, and Lemon, and Citron Trees; but all wild, and very few bearing any Fruit, at leaſt not then: However, the green Limes that I gathered, were not only pleasant to eat, but very wholesome; and I mix'd their Juice afterwards with Water, which made it very wholesome, and very cool, and refreshing.

I found now I had Business enough to gather and carry Home; and I resolv'd to lay up a Store, as well of Grapes, as Limes and Lemons, to furnish my self for the wet Season, which I knew was approaching.

In Order to this, I gather'd a great Heap of Grapes in one Place, and a lesser Heap in another Place, and a great Parcel of Limes and Lemons in another Place; and taking a few of each with me, I travell'd homeward, and resolv'd to come again, and bring a Bag or Sack, or what I could make to carry the reſt Home.

Accordingly, having spent three Days in this Journey, I came Home; so I muſt now call my Tent and my Cave: But, before I got thither, the Grapes were spoil'd, the Richness of the Fruits, and the Weight of the Juice having broken them, and bruis'd them, they were good for little or nothing; as to the Limes, they were good, but I could bring but a few.

The next Day, being the 19th, I went back, having made me two small Bags to bring Home my Harveſt: But I was surpriz'd, when coming to my Heap of Grapes, which were so rich and fine when I gather'd them, I found them all spread about, trod to Pieces; and dragg'd about some here, some there, and Abundance eaten and devour'd: By this I concluded, there were some wild Creatures thereabouts, which had done this; but what they were, I knew not.

However, as I found that there was no laying them up on Heaps, and no carrying them away in a Sack, but that one Way they would be deſtroy'd, and the other Way they would be crush'd with their own Weight, I took another Course; for I gather'd a large Quantity of the Grapes, and hung them up upon the out Branches of the Trees, that they might cure and dry in the Sun; and as for the Limes and Lemons, I carry'd as many back as I could well ſtand under.

When I came Home from this Journey, I contemplated with great Pleasure the Fruitfulness of that Valley, and the Pleasantness of the Situation, the Security from Storms on that Side the Water, and the Wood, and concluded, that I had pitch'd upon a Place to fix my Abode, which was by far the worſt Part of the Country. Upon the Whole I began to consider of removing my Habitation; and to look out for a Place equally safe, as where I now was situate, if possible, in that pleasant fruitful Part of the Island.

This Thought run long in my Head, and I was exceeding fond of it for some Time, the Pleasantness of the Place tempting me; but when I came to a nearer View of it, and to consider that I was now by the Sea-Side, where it was at leaſt possible that something might happen to my Advantage, and by the same ill Fate that brought me hither, might bring some other unhappy Wretches to the same Place; and tho' it was scarce probable that any such Thing should ever happen, yet to enclose my self among the Hills and Woods, in the Center of the Island, was to anticipate my Bondage, and to render such an Affair not only Improbable, but Impossible; and that therefore I ought not by any Means to remove.

However, I was so Enamour'd of this Place, that I

spent much of my Time there, for the whole remaining Part of the Month of *July*; and tho' upon second Thoughts I resolv'd as above, not to remove, yet I built me a little kind of a Bower, and surrounded it at a Distance with a strong Fence, being a double Hedge, as high as I could reach, well stak'd, and fill'd between with *Brushwood*; and here I lay very secure, sometimes two or three Nights together, always going over it with a Ladder, as before; so that I fancy'd now I had my Country-House, and my Sea-Coast-House: And this Work took me up to the Beginning of *August*.

I had but newly finish'd my Fence, and began to enjoy my Labour, but the Rains came on, and made me stick close to my first Habitation; for tho' I had made me a Tent like the other, with a Piece of a Sail, and spread it very well; yet I had not the Shelter of a Hill to keep me from Storms, nor a Cave behind me to retreat into, when the Rains were extraordinary.

About the Beginning of *August*, *as I said*, I had finish'd my Bower, and began to enjoy my self. The third of *August*, I found the Grapes I had hung up were perfectly dry'd, and indeed, were excellent good Raisins of the Sun; so I began to take them down from the Trees, and it was very happy that I did so; for the Rains which follow'd would have spoil'd them, and I had lost the best Part of my Winter Food; for I had above two hundred large Bunches of them. No sooner had I taken them all down, and carry'd most of them Home to my Cave, but it began to rain, and from hence, which was the fourteenth of *August*, it rain'd more or less, every Day, till the Middle of *October*; and sometimes so violently, that I could not stir out of my Cave for several Days.

In this Season I was much surpriz'd with the Increase

of my Family; I had been concern'd for the Loss of one
of my Cats, who run away from me, or as I thought had
been dead, and I heard no more Tale or Tidings of her,
till to my Aſtonishment she came Home about the End
of *Auguſt*, with three *Kittens*; this was the more ſtrange to
me, because tho' I had kill'd a wild Cat, as I call'd it, with
my Gun; yet I thought it was a quite differing Kind from
our *European* Cats; yet the young Cats were the same
Kind of House breed like the old one; and both my Cats
being Females, I thought it very ſtrange: But from these
three Cats, I afterwards came to be so peſter'd with Cats,
that I was forc'd to kill them like Vermine, or wild Beaſts,
and to drive them from my House as much as possible.

From the fourteenth of *Auguſt* to the twenty sixth, in-
cessant Rain, so that I could not ſtir, and was now very
careful not to be much wet. In this Confinement I began
to be ſtraitned for Food, but venturing out twice, I one
Day kill'd a Goat, and the laſt Day, which was the twenty
sixth, found a very large Tortoise, which was a Treat to
me, and my Food was regulated thus; I eat a Bunch of
Raisins for my Breakfaſt, a Piece of the Goat's Flesh, or
of the Turtle for my Dinner broil'd; for to my great Misfortune, I had no Vessel to boil or ſtew any Thing; and
two or three of the Turtle's Eggs for my Supper.

During this Confinement in my Cover, by the Rain, I
work'd daily two or three Hours at enlarging my Cave,
and by Degrees work'd it on towards one Side, till I came
to the Out-Side of the Hill, and made a Door or Way out,
which came beyond my Fence or Wall, and so I came in
and out this Way; but I was not perfeĉtly easy at lying so
open; for as I had manag'd my self before, I was in a per-
feĉt Enclosure, whereas now I thought I lay expos'd, and
open for any Thing to come in upon me; and yet I could

not perceive that there was any living Thing to fear, the biggeſt Creature that I had yet seen upon the Island being a Goat.

September the thirtieth, I was now come to the unhappy Anniversary of my Landing. I caſt up the Notches on my Poſt, and found I had been on Shore three hundred and sixty five Days. I kept this Day as a Solemn Faſt, setting it apart to Religious Exercise, proſtrating my self on the Ground with the moſt serious Humiliation, confessing my Sins to God, acknowledging his Righteous Judgments upon me, and praying to him to have Mercy on me, through Jesus Chriſt; and having not taſted the leaſt Refreshment for twelve Hours, even till the going down of the Sun, I then eat a Bisket Cake, and a Bunch of Grapes, and went to Bed, finishing the Day as I began it.

I had all this Time observ'd no Sabbath-Day; for as at firſt I had no Sense of Religion upon my Mind, I had after some Time omitted to diſtinguish the Weeks, by making a longer Notch than ordinary for the Sabbath-Day, and so did not really know what any of the Days were; but now having caſt up the Days, as above, I found I had been there a Year; so I divided it into Weeks, and set apart every seventh Day for a Sabbath; though I found at the End of my Account I had loſt a Day or two in my Reckoning.

A little after this my Ink began to fail me, and so I contented my self to use it more sparingly, and to write down only the moſt remarkable Events of my Life, without continuing a daily *Memorandum* of other Things.

The rainy Season, and the dry Season, began now to appear regular to me, and I learn'd to divide them so, as to provide for them accordingly. But I bought all my Experience before I had it; and this I am going to relate, was one of the moſt discouraging Experiments that I made at all: I have mention'd that I had sav'd the few Ears of Barley and Rice, which I had so surprizingly found spring up, as I thought, of themselves, and believe there was about thirty Stalks of Rice, and about twenty of Barley; and now I thought it a proper Time to sow it after the Rains, the Sun being in its *Southern* Position going from me.

Accordingly I dug up a Piece of Ground as well as I could with my wooden Spade, and dividing it into two Parts, I sow'd my Grain; but as I was sowing, it casually occur'd to my Thoughts, that I would not sow it all at firſt, because I did not know when was the proper Time for it; so I sow'd about two Thirds of the Seed, leaving about a Handful of each.

It was a great Comfort to me afterwards, that I did so, for not one Grain of that I sow'd this Time came to any Thing; for the dry Months following, the Earth having had no Rain after the Seed was sown, it had no Moiſture to assiſt its Growth, and never came up at all, till the wet Season had come again, and then it grew as if it had been but newly sown.

Finding my firſt Seed did not grow, which I easily imagin'd was by the Drought, I sought for a moiſter Piece of Ground to make another Trial in, and I dug up a Piece of Ground near my new Bower, and sow'd the reſt of my Seed in *February*, a little before the *Vernal Equinox;* and this having the rainy Months of *March* and *April* to water it, sprung up very pleasantly, and yielded a very good Crop; but having Part of the Seed left only, and not daring to sow all that I had, I had but a small Quantity at laſt, my whole Crop not amounting to above half a Peck of each kind.

But by this Experiment I was made Master of my Business, and knew exactly when the proper Season was to sow; and that I might expect two Seed Times, and two Harvests every Year.

While this Corn was growing, I made a little Discovery which was of use to me afterwards: As soon as the Rains were over, and the Weather began to settle, which was about the Month of *November*, I made a Visit up the Country to my Bower, where though I had not been some Months, yet I found all Things just as I left them. The Circle or double Hedge that I had made, was not only firm and entire; but the Stakes which I had cut out of some Trees that grew thereabouts, were all shot out and grown with long Branches, as much as a Willow-Tree usually shoots the first Year after lopping its Head. I could not tell what Tree to call it, that these Stakes were cut from. I was surpriz'd, and yet very well pleas'd, to see the young Trees grow; and I prun'd them, and led them up to grow as much alike as I could; and it is scarce credible how beautiful a Figure they grew into in three Years; so that though the Hedge made a Circle of about twenty five Yards in Diameter, yet the Trees, for such I might now call them, soon cover'd it; and it was a compleat Shade, sufficient to lodge under all the dry Season.

This made me resolve to cut some more Stakes, and make me a Hedge like this in a Semicircle round my Wall; I mean that of my first Dwelling, which I did; and placing the Trees or Stakes in a double Row, at about eight Yards distance from my first Fence, they grew presently, and were at first a fine Cover to my Habitation, and afterward serv'd for a Defence also, as I shall observe in its Order.

I found now, That the Seasons of the Year might generally be divided, not into *Summer* and *Winter*, as in *Europe*; but into the Rainy Seasons, and the Dry Seasons, which were generally thus,

Half *February,*
March, } Rainy, the *Sun* being then on, or near
Half *April,* the *Equinox.*

Half *April,*
May,
June, } Dry, the *Sun* being then to the *North* of
July, the Line.
Half *August,*

Half *August,*
September, } Rainy, the *Sun* being then come back.
Half *October,*

Half *October,*
November,
December, } Dry, the *Sun* being then to the *South* of
January, the Line.
Half *February,*

The Rainy Season sometimes held longer or shorter, as the Winds happen'd to blow; but this was the general Observation I made: After I had found by Experience, the ill Consequence of being abroad in the Rain, I took Care to furnish my self with Provisions before hand, that I might not be oblig'd to go out; and I sat within Doors as much as possible during the wet Months.

This Time I found much Employment, (and very suitable also to the Time) for I found great Occasion of many Things which I had no way to furnish my self with, but

by hard Labour and constant Application; particularly, I
try'd many Ways to make my self a Basket, but all the
Twigs I could get for the Purpose prov'd so brittle, that
they would do nothing. It prov'd of excellent Advantage
to me now, That when I was a Boy, I used to take great
Delight in standing at a *Basket-makers,* in the Town where
my Father liv'd, to see them make their *Wicker-ware;*
and being as Boys usually are, very officious to help, and
a great Observer of the Manner how they work'd those
Things, and sometimes lending a Hand, I had by this
Means full Knowledge of the Methods of it, that I wanted nothing but the Materials; when it came into my
Mind, That the Twigs of that Tree from whence I cut
my Stakes that grew, might possibly be as tough as the
Sallows, and *Willows,* and *Osiers* in *England,* and I resolv'd to try.

Accordingly the next Day, I went to my Country-
House, as I call'd it, and cutting some of the smaller
Twigs, I found them to my Purpose as much as I could
desire; whereupon I came the next Time prepar'd with a
Hatchet to cut down a Quantity, which I soon found, for
there was great Plenty of them; these I set up to dry within my Circle or Hedge, and when they were fit for Use, I
carry'd them to my Cave, and here during the next Season, I employ'd my self in making, *as well as I could,* a
great many Baskets, both to carry Earth, or to carry or
lay up any Thing as I had occasion; and tho' I did not
finish them very handsomly, yet I made them sufficiently
serviceable for my Purpose; and thus afterwards I took
Care never to be without them; and as my *Wicker-ware*
decay'd, I made more, especially, I made strong deep
Baskets to place my Corn in, instead of Sacks, when I
should come to have any Quantity of it.

Having mafter'd this Difficulty, and employ'd a World of Time about it, I beftirr'd my self to see if possible how to supply two Wants: I had no Vessels to hold any Thing that was Liquid, except two Runlets which were almoft full of Rum, and some Glass-Bottles, some of the common Size, and others which were Case-Bottles square, for the holding of Waters, Spirits, *&c.* I had not so much as a Pot to boil any Thing, except a great Kettle, which I sav'd out of the Ship, and which was too big for such Use as I desired.it, *viz.* To make Broth, and ftew a Bit of Meat by it self. The Second Thing I would fain have had, was a Tobacco-Pipe; but it was impossible to me to make one, however, I found a Contrivance for that too at laft.

I employ'd my self in Planting my Second Rows of Stakes or Piles and in this *Wicker* working all the Summer, or dry Season, when another Business took me up more Time than it could be imagin'd I could spare.

I mention'd before, That I had a great Mind to see the whole Island, and that I had travell'd up the Brook, and so on to where I built my Bower, and where I had an Opening quite to the Sea on the other Side of the Island; I now resolv'd to travel quite Cross to the Sea-Shore on that Side; so taking my Gun, a Hatchet, and my Dog, and a larger Quantity of Powder and Shot than usual, with two Bisket Cakes, and a great Bunch of Raisins in my Pouch for my Store, I began my Journey; when I had pass'd the Vale where my Bower ftood as above, I came within View of the Sea, to the *Weft*, and it being a very clear Day, I fairly descry'd Land, whether an Island or a Continent, I could not tell; but it lay very high, extending from the *Weft*, to the *W. S. W.* at a very great Distance; by my Guess it could not be less than Fifteen or Twenty Leagues off.

I could not tell what Part of the World this might be, otherwise than that I know it muſt be Part of *America*, and as I concluded by all my Observations, muſt be near the *Spanish* Dominions, and perhaps was all Inhabited by Savages, where if I should have landed, I had been in a worse Condition than I was now; and therefore I acquiesced in the Dispositions of Providence, which I began now to own, and to believe, order'd every Thing for the beſt; I say, I quieted my Mind with this, and left afflicting my self with Fruitless Wishes of being there.

Besides, after some Pause upon this Affair, I consider'd, that if this Land was the *Spanish* Coaſt, I should certainly, one Time or other, see some Vessel pass or repass one Way or other; but if not, then it was the *Savage* Coaſt between the *Spanish* Country and *Brasils*, which are indeed the worſt of *Savages*; for they are Cannibals, or Men-eaters, and fail not to murther and devour all the humane Bodies that fall into their Hands.

With these Considerations I walk'd very leisurely forward, I found that Side of the Island where I now was, much pleasanter than mine, the open or *Savanna* Fields sweet, adorn'd with Flowers and Grass, and full of very fine Woods. I saw Abundance of Parrots, and fain I would have caught one, if possible to have kept it to be tame, and taught it to speak to me. I did, after some Pains taking, catch a young Parrot, for I knock'd it down with a Stick, and having recover'd it, I brought it home; but it was some Years before I could make him speak: However, at laſt I taught him to call me by my Name very familiarly: But the Accident that follow'd, tho' it be a Trifle, will be very diverting in its Place.

I was exceedingly diverted with this Journey: I found in the low Grounds Hares, as I thought them to be, and

Foxes, but they differ'd greatly from all the other Kinds I
had met with; nor could I satisfy my self to eat them, tho'
I kill'd several: But I had no Need to be venturous; for I
had no Want of Food, and of that which was very good
too; especially these three Sorts, *viz.* Goats, Pidgeons,
and Turtle or Tortoise; which, added to my Grapes,
Leaden-hall Market could not have furnish'd a Table
better than I, in Proportion to the Company; and tho'
my Case was deplorable enough, yet I had great Cause
for Thankfulness, that I was not driven to any Extremities for Food; but rather Plenty, even to Dainties.

I never travell'd in this Journey above two Miles out-
right in a Day, or thereabouts; but I took so many Turns
and Returns, to see what Discoveries I could make, that
I came weary enough to the Place where I resolv'd to sit
down for all Night; and then I either repos'd my self in a
Tree, or surrounded my self with a Row of Stakes set upright in the Ground, either from one Tree to another, or
so as no wild Creature could come at me, without waking
me.

As soon as I came to the Sea Shore, I was surpriz'd to
see that I had taken up my Lot on the worſt Side of the
Island; for here indeed the Shore was cover'd with innumerable Turtles, whereas on the other Side I had found
but three in a Year and half. Here was also an infinite
Number of Fowls, of many Kinds, some which I had seen
and some which I had not seen of before, and many of
them very good Meat; but such as I knew not the Names
of, except those call'd *Penguins.*

I could have shot as many as I pleas'd, but was very
sparing of my Powder and Shot; and therefore had more
Mind to kill a she Goat, if I could, which I could better
feed on; and though there were many Goats here more

than on my Side the Island, yet it was with much more
Difficulty that I could come near them, the Country being flat and even, and they saw me much sooner than
when I was on the Hill.

I confess this Side of the Country was much pleasanter
than mine, but yet I had not the least Inclination to remove; for as I was fix'd in my Habitation, it became natural to me, and I seem'd all the while I was here, to be as it
were upon a Journey, and from Home: However, I travell'd along the Shore of the Sea, towards the *East*, I suppose about twelve Miles; and then setting up a great Pole
upon the Shore for a Mark, I concluded I would go
Home again; and that the next Journey I took should be
on the other Side of the Island, *East* from my Dwelling,
and so round till I came to my Post again: Of which in its
Place.

I took another Way to come back than that I went,
thinking I could easily keep all the Island so much in my
View, that I could not miss finding my first Dwelling by
viewing the Country; but I found my self mistaken; for
being come about two or three Miles, I found my self descended into a very large Valley; but so surrounded with
Hills, and those Hills cover'd with Wood, that I could
not see which was my Way by any Direction but that of
the Sun, nor even then, unless I knew very well the Position of the Sun at that Time of the Day.

It happen'd to my farther Misfortune, That the Weather prov'd hazey for three or four Days, while I was in
this Valley; and not being able to see the Sun, I wander'd
about very uncomfortably, and at last was oblig'd to find
out the Sea Side, look for my Post, and come back the
same Way I went; and then by easy Journies I turn'd
Homeward, the Weather being exceeding hot, and my

Gun, Ammunition, Hatchet, and other Things very heavy.

In this Journey my Dog surpriz'd a young Kid, and seiz'd upon it, and I running in to take hold of it, caught it, and sav'd it alive from the Dog; I had a great Mind to bring it Home if I could; for I had often been musing, Whether it might not be possible to get a Kid or two, and so raise a Breed of tame Goats, which might supply me when my Powder and Shot should be all spent.

I made a Collar to this little Creature, and with a String which I made of some Rope-Yarn, which I always carry'd about me, I led him along, tho' with some Difficulty, till I came to my Bower, and there I enclos'd him, and left him; for I was very impatient to be at Home, from whence I had been absent above a Month.

I cannot express what a Satisfaction it was to me, to come into my old Hutch, and lye down in my Hamock-Bed: This little wandring Journey, without settled Place of Abode, had been so unpleasant to me, that my own House, as I call'd it to my self, was a perfect Settlement to me, compar'd to that; and it rendred every Thing about me so comfortable, that I resolv'd I would never go a great Way from it again, while it should be my Lot to stay on the Island.

I repos'd my self here a Week, to rest and regale my self after my long Journey; during which, most of the Time was taken up in the weighty Affair of making a Cage for my Poll, who began now to be a meer Domestick, and to be mighty well acquainted with me. Then I began to think of the poor Kid, which I had penn'd in within my little Circle, and resolv'd to go and fetch it Home, or give it some Food; accordingly I went, and found it where I left it; for indeed it could not get out, but

almoſt ſtarv'd for want of Food: I went and cut Bows of
Trees, and Branches of such Shrubs as I could find, and
threw it over, and having fed it, I ty'd it as I did before, to
lead it away; but it was so tame with being hungry, that I
had no need to have ty'd it; for it follow'd me like a Dog;
and as I continually fed it, the Creature became so loving,
so gentle, and so fond, that it became from that Time one
of my Domeſticks also, and would never leave me afterwards.

The rainy Season of the *Autumnal Equinox* was now
come, and I kept the 30th. of *Sept.* in the same solemn
Manner as before, being the Anniversary of my Landing
on the Island, having now been there two Years, and no
more Prospeƈt of being deliver'd, than the firſt Day I
came there. I spent the whole Day in humble and thankful Acknowledgments of the many wonderful Mercies
which my Solitary Condition was attended with, and
without which it might have been infinitely more miserable. I gave humble and hearty Thanks that God had been
pleas'd to discover to me, even that it was possible I might
be more happy in this Solitary Condition, than I should
have been in a Liberty of Society, and in all the Pleasures
of the World. That he could fully make up to me, the
Deficiencies of my Solitary State, and the want of Humane Society by his Presence, and the Communications
of his Grace to my Soul, supporting, comforting, and encouraging me to depend upon his Providence here, and
hope for his Eternal Presence hereafter.

It was now that I began sensibly to feel how much
more happy this Life I now led was, with all its miserable
Circumſtances, than the wicked, cursed, abominable Life
I led all the paſt Part of my Days; and now I chang'd both
my Sorrows and my Joys; my very Desires alter'd, my

k

Affections chang'd their Gusts, and my Delights were perfectly new, from what they were at my first Coming, or indeed for the two Years past.

Before, as I walk'd about, either on my Hunting, or for viewing the Country; the Anguish of my Soul at my Condition, would break out upon me on a sudden, and my very Heart would die within me, to think of the Woods, the Mountains, the Desarts I was in; and how I was a Prisoner, lock'd up with the Eternal Bars and Bolts of the Ocean, in an uninhabited Wilderness, without Redemption: In the midst of the greatest Composures of my Mind, this would break out upon me like a Storm, and make me wring my Hands, and weep like a Child: Sometimes it would take me in the middle of my Work, and I would immediately sit down and sigh, and look upon the Ground for an Hour or two together; and this was still worse to me; for if I could burst out into Tears, or vent my self by Words, it would go off, and the Grief having exhausted it self would abate.

But now I began to exercise my self with new Thoughts; I daily read the Word of God, and apply'd all the Comforts of it to my present State: One Morning being very sad, I open'd the Bible upon these Words, *I will never, never leave thee, nor forsake thee*; immediately it occurr'd, That these Words were to me, Why else should they be directed in such a Manner, just at the Moment when I was mourning over my Condition, as one forsaken of God and Man? Well then, said I, if God does not forsake me, of what ill Consequence can it be, or what matters it, though the World should all forsake me, seeing on the other Hand, if I had all the World, and should lose the Favour and Blessing of God, there wou'd be no Comparison in the Loss.

From this Moment I began to conclude in my Mind, That it was possible for me to be more happy in this forsaken Solitary Condition, than it was probable I should ever have been in any other Particular State in the World; and with this Thought I was going to give Thanks to God for bringing me to this Place.

I know not what it was, but something shock'd my Mind at that Thought, and I durst not speak the Words: How canst thou be such a Hypocrite, (said I, even audibly) to pretend to be thankful for a Condition, which however thou may'st endeavour to be contented with, thou would'st rather pray heartily to be deliver'd from; so I stopp'd there: But though I could not say, I thank'd God for being there; yet I sincerely gave Thanks to God for opening my Eyes, by whatever afflicting Providences, to see the former Condition of my Life, and to mourn for my Wickedness, and repent. I never open'd the Bible, or shut it, but my very Soul within me, bless'd God for directing my Friend in *England*, without any Order of mine, to pack it up among my Goods; and for assisting me afterwards to save it out of the Wreck of the Ship.

Thus, and in this Disposition of Mind, I began my third Year; and tho' I have not given the Reader the Trouble of so particular Account of my Works this Year as the first; yet in General it may be observ'd, That I was very seldom idle; but having regularly divided my Time, according to the several daily Employments that were before me, such as, *First*, My Duty to God, and the Reading the Scriptures, which I constantly set apart some Time for thrice every Day. *Secondly*, The going Abroad with my Gun for Food, which generally took me up three Hours in every Morning, when it did not Rain. *Thirdly*, The ordering, curing, preserving, and cooking what I

had kill'd or catch'd for my Supply; these took up great
Part of the Day; also it is to be considered that the middle
of the Day when the Sun was in the *Zenith*, the Violence
of the Heat was too great to ſtir out; so that about four
Hours in the Evening was all the Time I could be suppos'd to work in; with this Exception, That sometimes I
chang'd my Hours of Hunting and Working, and went
to work in the Morning, and Abroad with my Gun in the
Afternoon.

To this short Time allow'd for Labour, I desire may
be added the exceeding Laboriousness of my Work; the
many Hours which for want of Tools, want of Help, and
want of Skill; every Thing I did, took up out of my Time:
For Example, I was full two and forty Days making me a
Board for a long Shelf, which I wanted in my Cave;
whereas two Sawyers with their Tools, and a Saw-Pit,
would have cut six of them out of the same Tree in half a
Day.

My Case was this, It was to be a large Tree, which was
to be cut down, because my Board was to be a broad one.
This Tree I was three Days a cutting down, and two more
cutting off the Bows, and reducing it to a Log, or Piece of
Timber. With inexpressible hacking and hewing I reduc'd both Sides of it into Chips, till it begun to be light
enough to move; than I turn'd it, and made one Side of it
smooth, and flat, as a Board from End to End; then turning that Side downward, cut the other Side, till I brought
the Plank to be about three Inches thick, and smooth on
both Sides. Any one may judge the Labour of my Hands
in such a Piece of Work; but Labour and Patience carry'd
me through that and many other Things: I only observe
this in Particular, to shew, The Reason why so much of
my Time went away with so little Work, *viz.* That what

might be a little to be done with Help and Tools, was a vaſt Labour, and requir'd a prodigious Time to do alone, and by hand.

But notwithſtanding this, with Patience and Labour I went through many Things; and indeed every Thing that my Circumſtances made necessary to me to do, as will appear by what follows.

I was now, in the Months of *November* and *December*, expeƈting my Crop of Barley and Rice. The Ground I had manur'd or dug up for them was not great; for as I observ'd, my Seed of each was not above the Quantity of half a Peck; for I had loſt one whole Crop by sowing in the dry Season; but now my Crop promis'd very well, when on a sudden I found I was in Danger of losing it all again by Enemies of several Sorts, which it was scarce possible to keep from it; as Firſt, The Goats, and wild Creatures which I call'd Hares, who taſting the Sweetness of the Blade, lay in it Night and Day, as soon as it came up, and eat it so close, that it could get no Time to shoot up into Stalk.

This I saw no Remedy for, but by making an Enclosure, about it with a Hedge, which I did with a great deal of Toil; and the more, because it requir'd Speed. However, as my ArableLand was but small, suited to my Crop, I got it totally well fenc'd, in about three Weeks Time; and shooting some of the Creatures in the Day Time, I set my Dog to guard it in the Night, tying him up to a Stake at the Gate, where he would ſtand and bark all Night long; so in a little Time the Enemies forsook the Place, and the Corn grew very ſtrong, and well, and began to ripen apace.

But as the Beaſts ruined me before, while my Corn was in the Blade; so the Birds were as likely to ruin me

now, when it was in the Ear; for going along by the Place
to see how it throve, I saw my little Crop surrounded with
Fowls of I know not how many sorts, who ſtood as it were
watching till I should be gone: I immediately let fly
among them (for I always had my Gun with me) I had no
sooner shot but there rose up a little Cloud of Fowls,
which I had not seen at all, from among the Corn it self.

This touch'd me sensibly, for I foresaw, that in a few
Days they would devour all my Hopes, that I should be
ſtarv'd, and never be able to raise a Crop at all, and what
to do I could not tell: However I resolv'd not to loose my
Corn, if possible, tho' I should watch it Night and Day.
In the firſt Place, I went among it to see what Damage
was already done, and found they had spoil'd a good deal
of it, but that as it was yet too Green for them, the Loss
was not so great, but that the Remainder was like to be a
good Crop if it could be sav'd.

I ſtaid by it to load my Gun, and then coming away I
could easily see the Thieves sitting upon all the Trees
about me, as if they only waited till I was gone away, and
the Event proved it to be so; for as I walk'd off as if I was
gone, I was no sooner out of their sight, but they dropt
down one by one into the Corn again. I was so provok'd
that I could not have Patience to ſtay till more came on,
knowing that every Grain that they eat now, was, *as it
might be said*, a Peck-load to me in the Consequence; but
coming up to the Hedge I fir'd again, and kill'd three of
them. This was what I wish'd for; so I took them up, and
serv'd them, as we serve notorious Thieves in *England*,
(*viz.*) Hang'd them in Chains for a Terror to others; it is
impossible to imagine almoſt, that this should have such
an Effeƈt, as it had; for the Fowls wou'd not only not
come at the Corn, but in short they forsook all that Part

of the Island, and I could never see a Bird near the Place
as long as my Scare-Crows hung there.

This I was very glad of, you may be sure, and about
the latter end of *December*, which was our second Harvest
of the Year, I reap'd my Crop.

I was sadly put to it for a Scythe or a Sicle to cut it down,
and all I could do was to make one as well as I could out
of one of the Broad Swords or Cutlasses, which I sav'd
among the Arms out of the Ship. However, as my first
Crop was but small I had no great Difficulty to cut it
down; in short, I reap'd it my Way, for I cut nothing off
but the Ears, and carry'd it away in a great Basket which
I had made, and so rubb'd it out with my Hands; and at
the End of all my Harvesting, I found that out of my half
Peck of Seed, I had near two Bushels of Rice, and above
two Bushels and half of Barley, *that is to say*, by my Guess,
for I had no Measure at that time.

However, this was a great Encouragement to me, and
I foresaw that in time, it wou'd please God to supply me
with Bread: And yet here I was perplex'd again, for I neither knew how to grind or make Meal of my Corn, or indeed how to clean it and part it; nor if made into Meal,
how to make Bread of it, and if how to make it, yet I knew
not how to bake it; these things being added to my Desire of having a good Quantity for Store, and to secure a
constant Supply, I resolv'd not to taste any of this Crop
but to preserve it all for Seed against the next Season, and
in the mean time to employ all my Study and Hours of
Working to accomplish this great Work of Providing
my self with Corn and Bread.

It might be truly said, that now I work'd for my Bread;
'tis a little wonderful, and what I believe few People have
thought much upon, (*viz.*) the strange multitude of little

Things necessary in the Providing, Producing, Curing, Dressing, Making and Finishing this one Article of Bread.

I that was reduced to a meer State of Nature, found this to my daily Discouragement, and was made more and more sensible of it every Hour, even after I had got the firſt Handful of Seed-Corn, which, as I have said, came up unexpeƈtedly, and indeed to a surprize.

Firſt, I had no Plow to turn up the Earth, no Spade or Shovel to dig it. Well, this I conquer'd, by making a wooden Spade, as I observ'd before; but this did my Work in but a wooden manner, and tho' it coſt me a great many Days to make it, yet for want of Iron it not only wore out the sooner, but made my Work the harder, and made it be perform'd much worse.

However this I bore with, and was content to work it out with Patience, and bear with the badness of the Performance. When the corn was sow'd, I had no Harrow, but was forced to go over it my self and drag a great heavy Bough of a Tree over it, to Scratch it, as it may be call'd, rather than Rake or Harrow it.

When it was growing and grown, I have observ'd already, how many things I wanted, to Fence it, Secure it, Mow or Reap it, Cure and Carry it Home, Thrash, Part it from the Chaff, and Save it. Then I wanted a Mill to Grind it, Sieves to Dress it, Yeaſt and Salt to make it into Bread, and an Oven to bake it, and yet all these things I did without, as shall be observ'd; and yet the Corn was an ineſtimable Comfort and Advantage to me too. All this, as I said, made every thing laborious and tedious to me, but that there was no help for; neither was my time so much Loss to me, because as I had divided it, a certain Part of it was every Day appointed to these Works; and as I resolv'd to use none of the Corn for Bread till I had a

greater Quantity by me, I had the next six Months to apply my self wholly by Labour and Invention to furnish
my self with Utensils proper for the performing all the
Operations necessary for the making the Corn (when I
had it) fit for my use.

But firſt, I was to prepare more Land, for I had now
Seed enough to sow above an Acre of Ground. Before I
did this, I had a Weeks-work at leaſt to make me a Spade,
which when it was done was but a sorry one indeed, and
very heavy, and requir'd double Labour to work with it;
however I went thro' that, and sow'd my Seed in two
large flat Pieces of Ground, as near my House as I could
find them to my Mind, and fenc'd them in with a good
Hedge, the Stakes of which were all cut of that Wood
which I had set before, and knew it would grow, so that
in one Year's time I knew I should have a Quick or Liv-
ing-Hedge, that would want but little Repair. This Work
was not so little as to take me up less than three Months,
because great Part of that time was of the wet Season,
when I could not go abroad.

Within Doors, *that is*, when it rained, and I could not
go out, I found Employment on the following Occasions;
always observing, that all the while I was at work I diverted my self with talking to my Parrot, and teaching him to
Speak, and I quickly learn'd him to know his own Name,
and at laſt to speak it out pretty loud P O L L, which was
the firſt Word I ever heard spoken in the Island by any
Mouth but my own. This therefore was not my Work,
but an assiſtant to my Work, for now, as I said, I had a
great Employment upon my Hands, as follows, (*viz.*) I
had long ſtudy'd by some Means or other, to make my
self some Earthen Vessels, which indeed I wanted sorely,
but knew not where to come at them : However, consider-

ing the Heat of the Climate, I did not doubt but if I could
find out any such Clay, I might botch up some such Pot,
as might, being dry'd in the Sun, be hard enough, and
strong enough to bear handling, and to hold any Thing
that was dry, and requir'd to be kept so; and as this was
necessary in the preparing Corn, Meal, &c. which was
the Thing I was upon, I resolv'd to make some as large
as I could, and fit only to stand like Jarrs to hold what
should be put into them.

It would make the Reader pity me, or rather laugh at
me, to tell how many awkward ways I took to raise this
Paste, what odd mishapen ugly things I made, how many
of them fell in, and how many fell out, the Clay not being
stiff enough to bear its own Weight; how many crack'd
by the over violent Heat of the Sun, being set out too hastily; and how many fell in pieces with only removing, as
well before as after they were dry'd; and in a word, how
after having labour'd hard to find the Clay, to dig it, to
temper it, it bring it home and work it; I could not make
above two large earthern ugly things, I cannot call them
Jarrs, in about two Months Labour.

However, as the Sun bak'd these Two, very dry and
hard, I lifted them very gently up, and set them down
again in two great Wicker-Baskets which I had made on
purpose for them, that they might not break, and as between the Pot and the Basket there was a little room to
spare, I stuff'd it full of the Rice and Barley Straw, and
these two Pots being to stand always dry, I thought would
hold my dry Corn, and perhaps the Meal, when the Corn
was bruised.

Tho' I miscarried so much in my Design for large
Pots, yet I made several smaller things with better Success, such as little round Pots, flat Dishes, Pitchers and

Pipkins, and any things my Hand turn'd to, and the Heat of the Sun bak'd them ſtrangely hard.

But all this would not answer my End, which was to get an earthern Pot to hold what was Liquid, and bear the Fire, which none of these could do. It happen'd after some time, making a pretty large Fire for cooking my Meat, when I went to put it out after I had done with it, I found a broken Piece of one of my Earthern-ware Vessels in the Fire, burnt as hard as a Stone, and red as a Tile. I was agreeably surpris'd to see it, and said to my self, that certainly they might be made to burn whole if they would burn broken.

This set me to ſtudying how to order my Fire, so as to make it burn me some Pots. I had no Notion of a Kiln, such as the Potters burn in, or of glazing them with Lead, tho' I had some Lead to do it with; but I plac'd three large Pipkins, and two or three Pots in a Pile one upon another, and plac'd my Fire-wood all round it with a great Heap of Embers under them; I ply'd the Fire with fresh Fuel round the out-side, and upon the top, till I saw the Pots in the inside red hot quite thro', and observ'd that they did not crack at all; when I saw them clear red, I let them ſtand in that Heat about 5 or 6 Hours, till I found one of them, tho' it did not crack, did melt or run, for the Sand which was mixed with the Clay melted by the violence of the Heat, and would have run into Glass if I had gone on; so I slack'd my Fire gradually till the Pots began to abate of the red Colour, and watching them all Night, that I might not let the Fire abate too faſt, in the Morning I had three very good, I will not say handsome Pipkins; and two other Earthen Pots, as hard burnt as cou'd be desir'd; and one of them perfeᦗly glaz'd with the Running of the Sand.

After this Experiment, I need not say that I wanted no sort of Earthern Ware for my Use; but I must needs say, as to the Shapes of them, they were very indifferent, as any one may suppose, when I had no way of making them; but as the Children make Dirt-Pies, or as a Woman would make Pies, that never learn'd to raise Past.

No Joy at a Thing of so mean a Nature was ever equal to mine, when I found I had made an Earthen Pot that would bear the Fire; and I had hardly Patience to stay till they were cold, before I set one upon the Fire again, with some Water in it, to boil me some Meat, which it did admirably well; and with a Piece of a Kid, I made some very good Broth, though I wanted Oatmeal, and several other Ingredients, requisite to make it so good as I would have had it been.

My next Concern was, to get me a Stone Mortar, to stamp or beat some Corn in; for as to the Mill, there was no thought at arriving to that Perfection of Art, with one Pair of Hands. To supply this Want I was at a great Loss; for of all Trades in the World I was as perfectly unquali- fy'd for a Stone-cutter, as for any whatever; neither had I any Tools to go about it with. I spent many a Day to find out a great Stone big enough to cut hollow, and make fit for a Mortar, and could find none at all; except what was in the solid Rock, and which I had no way to dig or cut out; nor indeed were the Rocks in the Island of Hard- ness sufficient, but were all of a sandy crumbling Stone, which neither would bear the Weight of a heavy Pestle, or would break the Corn without filling it with Sand; so after a great deal of Time lost in searching for a Stone. I gave it over, and resolv'd to look out for a great Block of hard Wood, which I found indeed much easier; and getting one as big as I had Strength to ſtir, I rounded it, and form'd it in the Out-side with my Axe and Hatchet, and then with the Help of Fire, and infinite Labour, made a hollow Place in it, as the *Indians* in *Brasil* make their *Canoes*. After this, I made a great heavy Peſtle or Beater, of the Wood call'd the Iron-wood, and this I prepar'd and laid by againſt I had my next Crop of Corn, when I propos'd to my self, to grind, or rather pound my Corn into Meal to make my Bread.

My next Difficulty was to make a Sieve, or Search, to dress my Meal, and to part it from the Bran, and the Husk, without which I did not see it possible I could have any Bread. This was a most difficult Thing, so much as but to think on; for to be sure I had nothing like the necessary Thing to make it; I mean fine thin Canvas, or Stuff, to search the Meal through. And here I was at a full Stop for many Months; nor did I really know what to do; Linnen I had none left, but what was meer Rags; I had Goats Hair, but neither knew I how to weave it, or spin it; and had I known how, here was no Tools to work it with; all the Remedy that I found for this, was, That at laſt I did remember I had among the Seamens Cloaths which were sav'd out of the Ship, some Neckcloths of Callicoe, or Muslin; and with some Pieces of these, I made three small Sieves, but proper enough for the Work; and thus I made shift for some Years; how I did afterwards, I shall shew in its Place.

The baking part was the next Thing to be consider'd, and how I should make Bread when I came to have Corn; for firſt I had no Yeaſt; as to that Part, as there was no supplying the Want, so I did not concern my self much about it; But for an Oven, I was indeed in great Pain, at length I found out an Experiment for that also, which

was this; I made some Earthern Vessels very broad, but
not deep; that is to say, about two Foot Diameter, and
not above nine Inches deep; these I burnt in the Fire, as I
had done the other, and laid them by; and when I wanted
to bake, I made a great Fire upon my Hearth, which I had
pav'd with some square Tiles of my own making, and
burning also; but I should not call them square.

When the Fire-wood was burnt pretty much into Em-
bers, or live Coals, I drew them forward upon this Hearth
so as to cover it all over, and there I let them lye, till the
Hearth was very hot, then sweeping away all the Embers,
I set down my Loaf, or Loaves, and whelming down the
Earthen Pot upon them, drew the Embers all round the
Out-side of the Pot, to keep in, and add to the Heat; and
thus, as well as in the beſt Oven in the World, I bak'd my
Barley Loaves, and became in little Time a meer Paſtry-
Cook into the Bargain; for I made my self several Cakes
of the Rice, and Puddings; indeed I made no Pies, nei-
ther had I any Thing to put into them, supposing I had,
except the Flesh either of Fowls or Goats.

It need not be wondred at, if all these Things took me
up moſt Part of the third Year of my Abode here; for it is
to be observ'd, That in the Intervals of these Things, I
had my new Harveſt and Husbandry to manage; for I
reap'd my Corn in its Season, and carry'd it Home as
well as I could, and laid it up in the Ear, in my large
Baskets, till I had Time to rub it out; for I had no Floor
to thrash it on, or Inſtrument to thrash it with.

And now indeed my Stock of Corn increasing, I really
wanted to build my Barns bigger. I wanted a Place to lay
it up in; for the Increase of the Corn now yielded me so
much, that I had of the Barley about twenty Bushels, and
of the Rice as much, or more; insomuch, that now I re-

solv'd to begin to use it freely; for my Bread had been
quite gone a great while; Also I resolv'd to see what
Quantity would be sufficient for me a whole Year, and to
sow but once a Year.

Upon the whole, I found that the forty Bushels of Barley and Rice, was much more than I could consume in a
Year; so I resolv'd to sow juſt the same Quantity every
Year, that I sow'd the laſt, in Hopes that such a Quantity
would fully provide me with Bread, *&c.*

All the while these Things were doing, you may be
sure my Thoughts run many times upon the Prospeſt of
Land which I had seen from the other Side of the Island,
and I was not without secret Wishes that I were on Shore
there, fancying the seeing the main Land, and in an inhabited Country, I might find some Way or other to convey myself farther, and perhaps at laſt find some Means
of Escape.

But all this while I made no Allowance for the Dangers
of such a Condition, and how I might fall into the Hands
of Savages, and perhaps such as I might have Reason to
think far worse than the Lions and Tigers of *Africa.* That
if I once came into their Power, I should run a Hazard
more than a thousand to one of being kill'd, and perhaps
of being eaten; for I had heard that the People of the *Car-
ribean* Coaſt were Canibals, or Man-eaters; and I knew
by the Latitude that I could not be far off from that Shore.
That suppose they were not Canibals, yet that they might
kill me, as many *Europeans* who had fallen into their
Hands had been serv'd, even when they had been ten or
twenty together; much more I that was but one, and
could make little or no Defence: All these Things, I say,
which I ought to have consider'd well of, and did caſt up
in my Thoughts afterwards, yet took up none of my Ap-

prehensions at firſt; but my Head run mightily upon the Thought of getting over to the Shore.

Now I wish'd for my Boy *Xury*, and the long Boat, with the Shoulder of Mutton Sail, with which I sail'd above a thousand Miles on the Coaſt of *Africk*; but this was in vain. Then I thought I would go and look at our Ship's Boat, which, as I have said, was blown up upon the Shore, a great Way in the Storm, when we were firſt caſt away. She lay almoſt where she did at firſt, but not quite; and was turn'd by the Force of the Waves and the Winds almoſt Bottom upward, againſt a high Ridge of Beachy rough Sand; but no Water about her as before.

If I had had Hands to have refitted her, and to have launch'd her into the Water, the Boat would have done well enough, and I might have gone back into the *Brasils* with her easily enough; but I might have foreseen, That I could no more turn her, and set her upright upon her Bottom, than I could remove the Island: However, I went to the Woods, and cut Levers and Rollers, and brought them to the Boat, resolv'd to try what I could do, suggesting to my self, That if I could but turn her down, I might easily repair the Damage she had receiv'd, and she would be a very good Boat, and I might go to Sea in her very easily.

I spar'd no Pains indeed, in this Piece of fruitless Toil, and spent, I think, three or four Weeks about it; at laſt finding it impossible to heave it up with my little Strength, I fell to digging away the Sand, to undermine it, and so to make it fall down, setting Pieces of Wood to thruſt and guide it right in the Fall.

But when I had done this, I was unable to ſtir it up again, or to get under it, much less to move it forward, towards the Water; so I was forc'd to give it over; and yet, though I gave over the Hopes of the Boat, my desire to venture over for the Main increased, rather than decreased, as the Means for it seem'd impossible.

This at length put me upon thinking, Whether it was not possible to make my self a *Canoe*, or *Periagua*, such as the Natives of those Climates make, even without Tools, or, as I might say, without Hands, *viz.* of the Trunk of a great Tree. This I not only thought possible, but easy, and pleas'd my self extreamly with the Thoughts of making it, and with my having much more Convenience for it than any of the *Negroes* or *Indians*; but not at all considering the particular Inconveniences which I lay under, more than the *Indians* did, *viz.* Want of Hands to move it, when it was made, into the Water, a Difficulty much harder for me to surmount, than all the Consequences of Want of Tools could be to them; for what was it to me, That when I had chosen a vaſt Tree in the Woods, I might with much Trouble cut it down, if after I might be able with my Tools to hew and dub the Outside into the proper Shape of a Boat, and burn or cut out the In-side to make it hollow, so to make a Boat of it: If after all this, I muſt leave it juſt there where I found it, and was not able to launch it into the Water.

One would have thought, I could not have had the leaſt Reflection upon my Mind of my Circumſtance, while I was making this Boat; but I should have immediately thought how I should get it into the Sea; but my Thoughts were so intent upon my Voyage over the Sea in it, that I never once consider'd how I should get it off of the Land; and it was really in its own Nature more easy for me to guide it over forty five Miles of Sea, than about forty five Fathom of Land, where it lay, to set it a float in the Water.

l

I went to work upon this Boat, the moſt like a Fool, that ever Man did, who had any of his Senses awake. I pleas'd my self with the Design, without determining whether I was ever able to undertake it; not but that the Difficulty of launching my Boat came often into my Head; but I put a ſtop to my own Enquiries into it, by this foolish Answer which I gave my self, *Let's firſt make it, I'll warrant I'll find some Way or other to get it along, when 'tis done.*

This was a moſt prepoſterous Method; but the Eager-ness of my Fancy prevail'd, and to work I went. I fell'd a Cedar Tree: I queſtion much whether *Solomon* ever had such a One for the Building of the Temple at *Jerusalem.* It was five Foot ten Inches Diameter at the lower Part next the Stump, and four Foot eleven Inches Diameter at the End of twenty two Foot, after which it lessen'd for a while, and then parted into Branches: It was not without infinite Labour that I fell'd this Tree: I was twenty Days hacking and hewing at it at the Bottom. I was fourteen more getting the Branches and Limbs, and the vaſt spreading Head of it cut off, which I hack'd and hew'd through with Axe and Hatchet, and inexpressible La-bour: After this, it coſt me a Month to shape it, and dub it to a Proportion, and to something like the Bottom of a Boat, that it might swim upright as it ought to do. It coſt me near three Months more to clear the In-side, and work it out so, as to make an exaƈt Boat of it: This I did indeed without Fire, by meer Malett and Chissel, and by the dint of hard Labour, till I had brought it to be a very handsome *Periagua,* and big enough to have carry'd six and twenty Men, and consequently big enough to have carry'd me and all my Cargo.

When I had gone through this Work, I was extremely

delighted with it. The Boat was really much bigger than
I ever saw a *Canoe*, or *Periagua*, that was made of one
Tree, in my Life. Many a weary Stroke it had coſt, you
may be sure; and there remain'd nothing but to get it into
the Water; and had I gotten it into the Water, I make no
queſtion but I should have began the maddeſt Voyage,
and the moſt unlikely to be perform'd, that ever was undertaken.

But all my Devices to get it into the Water fail'd me;
tho' they coſt me infinite Labour too. It lay about one
hundred Yards from the Water, and not more: But the
firſt Inconvenience was, it was up Hill towards the Creek;
well, take to away this Discouragement, I resolv'd to dig
into the Surface of the Earth, and so make a Declivity:
This I begun, and it coſt me a prodigious deal of Pains;
but who grutches Pains, that have their Deliverance in
View: But when this was work'd through, and this Difficulty manag'd, it was ſtill much at one; for I could no
more ſtir the *Canoe*, than I could the other Boat.

Then I measur'd the Diſtance of Ground, and resolv'd
to cut a Dock, or Canal, to bring the Water up to the *Canoe*, seeing I could not bring the *Canoe* down to the Water: Well, I began this Work, and when I began to enter
into it, and calculate how deep it was to be dug, how
broad, how the Stuff to be thrown out, I found, That by
the Number of Hands I had, being none but my own, it
muſt have been ten or twelve Years before I should have
gone through with it; for the Shore lay high, so that at
the upper End, it muſt have been at leaſt twenty Foot
Deep; so at length, tho' with great Reluċtancy, I gave
this Attempt over also.

This griev'd me heartily, and now I saw, tho' too late,
the Folly of beginning a Work before we count the Coſt;

and before we judge rightly of our own Strength to go through with it.

In the middle of this Work, I finish'd my fourth Year in this Place, and kept my Anniversary with the same Devotion, and with as much Comfort as ever before; for by a constant Study, and serious Application of the Word of God, and by the Assistance of his Grace, I gain'd a different Knowledge from what I had before. I entertain'd different Notions of Things. I look'd now upon the World as a Thing remote, which I had nothing to do with, no Expectation from, and indeed no Desires about: In a Word, I had nothing indeed to do with it, nor was ever like to have; so I thought it look'd as we may perhaps look upon it hereafter, *viz.* as a Place I had liv'd in, but was come out of it; and well might I say, as Father *Abraham* to *Dives, Between me and thee is a great Gulph fix'd.*

In the first Place, I was remov'd from all the Wickedness of the World here. I had neither the *Lust of the Flesh, the Lust of the Eye, or the Pride of Life.* I had nothing to covet; for I had all that I was now capable of enjoying: I was Lord of the whole Manor; or if I pleas'd, I might call my self King, or Emperor over the whole Country which I had Possession of. There were no Rivals. I had no Competitor, none to dispute Sovereignty or Command with me. I might have rais'd Ship Loadings of Corn; but I had no use for it; so I let as little grow as I thought enough for my Occasion. I had Tortoise or Turtles enough; but now and then one, was as much as I could put to any use. I had Timber enough to have built a Fleet of Ships. I had Grapes enough to have made Wine, or to have cur'd into Raisins, to have loaded that Fleet, when they had been built.

But all I could make use of, was, All that was valuable. I had enough to eat, and to supply my Wants, and, what was all the reſt to me? If I kill'd more Flesh than I could eat, the Dog muſt eat it, or the Vermin. If I sow'd more Corn than I could eat, it muſt be spoil'd. The Trees that I cut down, were lying to rot on the Ground. I could make no more use of them than for Fewel; and that I had no Occasion for, but to dress my Food.

In a Word, The Nature and Experience of Things dictated to me upon juſt Reflection, That all the good Things of this World, are no farther good to us, than they are for our Use; and that whatever we may heap up indeed to give others, we enjoy juſt as much as we can use, and no more. The moſt covetous griping Miser in the World would have been cur'd of the Vice of Covetousness, if he had been in my Case; for I possess'd infinitely more than I knew what to do with. I had no room for Desire, except it was of Things which I had not, and they were but Trifles, though indeed of great Use to me. I had, as I hinted before, a Parcel of Money, as well Gold as Silver, about thirty six Pounds Sterling: Alas! There the naſty sorry useless Stuff lay; I had no manner of Business for it; and I often thought with my self, That I would have given a Handful of it for a Gross of Tobacco-Pipes, or for a Hand-Mill to grind my Corn; nay, I would have given it all for Sixpennyworth of *Turnip* and *Carrot* Seed out of *England*, or for a Handful of *Pease* and *Beans*, and a Bottle of Ink: *As it was*, I had not the leaſt Advantage by it, or Benefit from it; but there it lay in a Drawer, and grew mouldy with the Damp of the Cave, in the wet Season; and if I had had the Drawer full of Diamonds, it had been the same Case; and they had been of no manner of Value to me, because of no Use.

I had now brought my State of Life to be much easier in itself than it was at firſt, and much easier to my Mind, as well as to my Body. I frequently sat down to my Meat with Thankfulness, and admir'd the Hand of God's Providence, which had thus spread my Table in the Wilderness. I learn'd to look more upon the bright Side of my Condition, and less upon the dark Side; and to consider what I enjoy'd, rather than what I wanted; and this gave me sometimes such secret Comforts, that I cannot express them; and which I take Notice of here, to put those discontented People in Mind of it, who cannot enjoy comfortably what God has given them; because they see, and covet something that he has not given them: All our Discontents about what we want, appear'd to me, to spring from the Want of Thankfulness for what we have.

Another Refleᵻtion was of great Use to me, and doubtless would be so to any one that should fall into such Distress as mine was; and this was, To compare my present Condition with what I at firſt expeᵻted it should be; nay, with what it would certainly have been, if the good Providence of God had not wonderfully order'd the Ship to be caſt up nearer to the Shore, where I not only could come at her, but could bring what I got out of her to the Shore, for my Relief and Comfort; without which I had wanted for Tools to work, Weapons for Defence, or Gun-Powder and Shot for getting my Food.

I spent whole Hours, I may say whole Days, in representing to my self in the moſt lively Colours, how I muſt have aᵻted, if I had got nothing out of the Ship. How I could not have so much as got any Food, except Fish and Turtles; and that as it was long before I found any of them, I muſt have perish'd firſt. That I should have liv'd, if I had not perish'd, like a meer Savage. That if I had

kill'd a Goat, or a Fowl, by any Contrivance, I had no
way to flea or open them, or part the Flesh from the Skin,
and the Bowels, or to cut it up; but muſt gnaw it with my
Teeth, and pull it with my Claws like a Beaſt.

These Reflections made me very sensible of the Goodness of Providence to me, and very thankful for my present Condition, with all its Hardships and Misfortunes:
And this Part also I cannot but recommend to the Reflection of those, who are apt in their Misery to say, *Is
any Affliction like mine!* Let them consider, How much
worse the Cases of some People are, and their Case might
have been, if Providence had thought fit.

I had another Reflection which assiſted me also to comfort my Mind with Hopes; and this was, comparing my
present Condition with what I had deserv'd, and had
therefore Reason to expect from the Hand of Providence. I had liv'd a dreadful Life, perfectly deſtitute of
the Knowledge and Fear of God. I had been well inſtruct-
ed by Father and Mother; neither had they been wanting
to me, in their early Endeavours, to infuse a religious
Awe of God into my Mind, a Sense of my Duty, and of
what the Nature and End of my Being requir'd of me.
But alas! falling early into the Seafaring Life, which of
all the Lives is the moſt deſtitute of the Fear of God,
though his Terrors are always before them; I say, falling
early into the Seafaring Life, and into Seafaring Company, all that little Sense of Religion which I had entertain'd, was laugh'd out of me by my Mess-Mates, by a
harden'd despising of Dangers; and the Views of Death,
which grew habitual to me; by my long Absence from all
Manner of Opportunities to converse with any thing but
what was like my self, or to hear any thing that was good,
or tended towards it.

So void was I of every Thing that was good, or of the leaſt Sense of what I was, or was to be, that in the greateſt Deliverances I enjoy'd, such as my Escape from *Sallee;* my being taken up by the *Portuguese* Maſter of the Ship; my being planted so well in the *Brasils*; my receiving the Cargo from *England*, and the like; I never had once the Word *Thank God*, so much as on my Mind, or in my Mouth; nor in the greateſt Diſtress, had I so much as a Thought to pray to him, or so much as to say, *Lord have Mercy upon me*; no nor to mention the Name of God, unless it was to swear by, and blaspheme it.

I had terrible Reflections upon my Mind for many Months, as I have already observ'd, on the Account of my wicked and hardned Life paſt; and when I look'd about me and considered what particular Providences had attended me since my coming into this Place, and how God had dealt bountifully with me; had not only punished me less than my Iniquity had deserv'd, but had so plentifully provided for me; this gave me great hopes that my Repentance was accepted, and that God hath yet Mercy in ſtore for me.

With these Reflections I work'd my Mind up, not only to Resignation to the Will of God in the present Disposition of my Circumſtances; but even to a sincere Thankfulness for my Condition, and that I who was yet a living Man, ought not to complain, seeing I had not the due Punishment of my Sins; that I enjoy'd so many Mercies which I had no reason to have expeſted in that Place; that I ought never more to repine at my Condition but to rejoyce, and to give daily Thanks for that daily Bread, which nothing but a Croud of Wonders could have brought. That I ought to consider I had been fed even by Miracle, even as great as that of feeding *Elijah* by Ra-

vens; nay, by a long Series of Miracles, and that I could
hardly have nam'd a Place in the unhabitable Part of the
World where I could have been caſt more to my Advantage: A Place, where as I had no Society, which was my
Afflicion on one Hand, so I found no ravenous Beaſt, no
furious Wolves or Tygers to threaten my Life, no venomous Creatures or poisonous, which I might feed on to my
Hurt, no Savages to murther and devour me.

In a word, as my Life was a Life of Sorrow, one way, so
it was a Life of Mercy, another; and I wanted nothing to
make it a Life of Comfort, but to be able to make my
Sence of God's Goodness to me, and Care over me in this
Condition, be my daily Consolation; and after I did make
a juſt Improvement of these things, I went away and was
no more sad.

I had now been here so long, that many Things which
I brought on Shore for my Help, were either quite gone,
or very much waſted and near spent.

My Ink, as I observed, had been gone some time, all
but a very little, which I eek'd out with Water a little and
a little, till it was so pale it scarce left any Appearance of
black upon the Paper: As long as it laſted, I made use of
it to minute down the Days of the Month on which any
remarkable Thing happen'd to me, and firſt by caſting
up Times paſt: I remember that there was a ſtrange Con-
currence of Days, in the various Providences which befel
me; and which, if I had been superſtitiously inclin'd to
observe Days as Fatal or Fortunate, I might have had
Reason to have look'd upon with a great deal of Curiosity.

Firſt, I had observed, that the same Day that I broke
away from my Father and my Friends, and run away to
Hull, in order to go to Sea; the same Day afterwards I
was taken by the *Sallee* Man of War, and made a Slave.

The same Day of the Year that I escaped out of the Wreck of that Ship in *Yarmouth* Roads, that same Day-Year afterwards I made my escape from *Sallee* in the Boat.

The same Day of the Year I was born on (*viz.*) the 30*th* of *September*, that same Day, I had my Life so miraculously saved 26 Year after, when I was cast on Shore in this Island, so that my wicked Life, and my solitary Life begun both on a Day.

The next Thing to my Ink's, being wasted, was that of my Bread, I mean the Bisket which I brought out of the Ship; This I had husbanded to the last Degree, allowing my self but one Cake of Bread a Day for above a Year, and yet I was quite without Bread for near a Year before I got any Corn of my own, and great Reason I had to be thankful that I had any at all, the getting it being, as has been already observed, next to miraculous.

My Cloaths began to decay too mightily: As to Linnen, I had had none a good while, except some chequer'd Shirts which I found in the Chests of the other Seamen, and which I carefully preserved, because many times I could bear no other Cloaths on but a Shirt; and it was a very great help to me that I had among all the Men's Cloaths of the Ship almost three dozen of Shirts. There were also several thick Watch Coats of the Seamens, which were left indeed, but they were too hot to wear; and tho' it is true, that the Weather was so violent hot, that there was no need of Cloaths, yet I could not go quite naked; no, tho' I had been inclin'd to it, which I was not, nor could not abide the thoughts of it, tho' I was all alone.

The Reason why I could not go quite naked, was, I could not bear the heat of the Sun so well when quite naked, as with some Cloaths on; nay, the very Heat fre-

quently blistered my Skin; whereas with a Shirt on, the
Air itself made some Motion and, whistling under that
Shirt was twofold cooler than without it: no more could I
ever bring my self to go out in the heat of Sun, without a
Cap or a Hat; the heat of the Sun beating with such Violence as it does in that Place, would give me the Head-
ach presently, by darting so directly on my Head, without a Cap or Hat on, so that I could not bear it, whereas,
if I put on my Hat, it would presently go away.

Upon those Views I began to consider about putting
the few Rags I had, which I call'd Cloaths, into some
Order; I had worn out all the Wastcoats I had, and my
Business was now to try if I could not make Jackets out
of the great Watch-Coats which I had by me, and with
such other Materials as I had, so I set to Work a Tayler-
ing, or rather indeed a Botching, for I made most piteous
Work of it. However, I made shift to make two or three
new Wastcoats, which I hoped wou'd serve me a great
while; as for Breeches or Drawers, I made but a very sorry shift indeed, till afterward.

I have mentioned that I saved the Skins of all the Creatures that I kill'd, I mean four-footed ones, and I had
hung them up stretch'd out with Sticks in the Sun, by
which means some of them were so dry and hard that
they were fit for little, but others it seems were very useful. The first thing I made of these was a great Cap for my
Head, with the Hair on the out Side to shoor off the Rain;
and this I perform'd so well, that after this I made me a
Suit of Cloaths wholly of these Skins, that is to say, a
Wastcoat, and Breeches open at Knees, and both loose,
for they were rather wanting to keep me cool than to keep
me warm. I must not omit to acknowledge that they were
wretchedly made; for if I was a bad *Carpenter*, I was a

worse *Taylor*. However, they were such as I made very
good shift with; and when I was abroad, if it happen'd to
rain, the Hair of my Waſtcoat and Cap being outermoſt,
I was kept very dry.

After this I spent a great deal of Time and Pains to
make me an Umbrella; I was indeed in great want of one,
and had a great Mind to make one; I had seen them made
in the *Brasils*, where they are very useful in the great
Heats which are there. And I felt the Heats every jot as
great here, and greater too, being nearer the Equinox;
besides, as I was oblig'd to be much abroad, it was a moſt
useful thing to me, as well for the Rains as the Heats. I
took a world of Pains at it, and was a great while before I
could make anything likely to hold; nay, after I thought
I had hit the Way, I spoil'd 2 or 3 before I made one to
my Mind; but at laſt I made one that answer'd indiffer-
ently well: The main Difficulty I found was to make it to
let down. I could make it to spread, but if it did not let
down too, and draw in, it was not portable for me any
Way but juſt over my Head, which wou'd not do. However, at laſt, as I said, I made one to answer, and covered
it with Skins, the Hair upwards, so that it caſt off the
Rains like a Penthouse, and kept off the Sun so effeƈtually, that I could walk out in the hotteſt of the Weather
with greater Advantage than I could before in the cooleſt,
and when I had no need of it, cou'd close it and carry it
under my Arm.

Thus I liv'd mighty comfortably, my Mind being entirely composed by resigning to the Will of God, and
throwing my self wholly upon the Disposal of his Providence. This made my Life better than sociable, for when
I began to regret the want of Conversation, I would ask
my self whether thus conversing mutually with my own

Thoughts, and, as I hope I may say, with even God himself by Ejaculations, was not better than the utmost En-
joyment of humane Society in the World.

I cannot say that after this, for five Years, any extraordinary thing happened to me, but I liv'd on in the same
Course, in the same Posture and Place, just as before; the
chief things I was employ'd in, besides my yearly Labour
of planting my Barley and Rice, and curing my Raisins,
of both which I always kept up just enough to have sufficient Stock of one Year's Provisions beforehand. I say,
besides this yearly Labour, and my daily Labour of going out with my Gun, I had one Labour to make me a
Canoe, which at last I finished. So that by digging a Canal to it of six Foot wide, and four Foot deep, I brought it
into the Creek, almost half a Mile. As for the first, which
was so vastly big, as I made it without considering beforehand, as I ought to do, how I should be able to launch it;
so never being able to bring it to the Water, or bring the
Water to it, I was oblig'd to let it lye where it was, as a
Memorandum to teach me to be wiser next Time: Indeed,
the next Time, tho' I could not get a Tree proper for it,
and in a Place where I could not get the Water to it, at
any less Distance, than as I have said, near half a Mile;
yet as I saw it was practicable at last, I never gave it over;
and though I was near two Years about it, yet I never
grutch'd my Labour, in Hopes of having a Boat to go
off to Sea at last.

However, though my little *Periagua* was finish'd; yet
the Size of it was not at all answerable to the Design
which I had in View, when I made the first; I mean, Of
venturing over to the *Terra Firma*, where it was above
forty Miles broad; accordingly, the Smallness of my
Boat assisted to put an End to that Design, and now I

thought no more of it: But as I had a Boat, my next Design was to make a Tour round the Island; for as I had
been on the other Side, in one Place, crossing as I have
already describ'd it, over the Land; so the Discoveries I
made in that little Journey, made me very eager to see
other Parts of the Coaſt; and now I had a Boat, I thought
of nothing but sailing round the Island.

For this Purpose, that I might do every Thing with
Discretion and Consideration, I fitted up a little Maſt to
my Boat, and made a Sail to it, out of some of the Pieces
of the Ship's Sail, which lay in ſtore; and of which I had a
great Stock by me.

Having fitted my Maſt and Sail, and try'd the Boat, I
found she would sail very well: Then I made little Lockers, or Boxes, at either End of my Boat, to put Provisions,
Necessaries and Ammunition, &c. into, to be kept dry,
either from Rain, or the Sprye of the Sea; and a little long
hollow Place I cut in the In-side of the Boat, where I
could lay my Gun, making a Flap to hang down over it to
keep it dry.

I fix'd my Umbrella also in a Step at the Stern, like a
Maſt, to ſtand over my Head, and keep the Heat of the
Sun off of me like an Auning; and thus I every now and
then took a little Voyage upon the Sea, but never went far
out, nor far from the little Creek; but at laſt being eager
to view the Circumference of my little Kingdom, I resolv'd upon my Tour, and accordingly I victuall'd my
Ship for the Voyage, putting in two Dozen of my Loaves
(Cakes I should rather call them) of Barley Bread, an
Earthen Pot full of parch'd Rice, a Food I eat a great deal
of, a little Bottle of Rum, half a Goat, and Powder and
Shot for killing more, and two large Watch-coats, of
those which, as I mention'd before, I had sav'd out of the

Seamen's Chests; these I took, one to lye upon, and the other to cover me in the Night.

It was the sixth of *November*, in the sixth Year of my Reign, or my Captivity, which you please, That I set out on this Voyage, and I found it much longer than I expected; for though the Island it self was not very large, yet when I came to the *East* Side of it, I found a great Ledge of Rocks lye out above two Leagues into the Sea, some above Water, some under it; and beyond that, a Shoal of Sand, lying dry half a League more; so that I was oblig'd to go a great Way out to Sea to double the Point.

When first I discover'd them, I was going to give over my Enterprise, and come back again, not knowing how far it might oblige me to go out to Sea; and above all, doubting how I should get back again; so I came to an Anchor; for I had made me a kind of an Anchor with a Piece of a broken Graplin, which I got out of the Ship.

Having secur'd my Boat, I took my Gun, and went on Shore, climbing up upon a Hill, which seem'd to over-look that Point, where I saw the full Extent of it, and re-solv'd to venture.

In my viewing the Sea from that Hill where I stood, I perceiv'd a strong, and indeed, a most furious Current, which run to the *East*, and even came close to the Point; and I took the more Notice of it, because I saw there might be some Danger; that when I came into it, I might be carry'd out to Sea by the Strength of it, and not be able to make the Island again; and indeed, had I not gotten first up upon this Hill, I believe it would have been so; for there was the same Current on the other Side the Is-land, only, that it set off at a farther Distance; and I saw there was a strong Eddy under the Shore; so I had nothing to do but to get in out of the firſt Current, and I should presently be in an Eddy.

I lay here, however, two Days; because the Wind blowing pretty fresh at *E. S. E.* and that being juſt contrary to the said Current, made a great Breach of the Sea upon the Point; so that it was not safe for me to keep too close to the Shore for the Breach, nor to go too far off because of the Stream.

The Third Day in the Morning, the Wind having abated over Night, the Sea was calm, and I ventur'd; but I am a warning Piece again, to all rash and ignorant Pilots; for no sooner was I come to the Point, when even I was not my Boat's Length from the Shore, but I found my self in a great Depth of Water, and a Current like the Sluice of a Mill: It carry'd my Boat a long with it with such Violence, That all I could do, could not keep her so much as on the Edge of it; but I found it hurry'd me farther and farther out from the Eddy, which was on my left Hand. There was no Wind ſtirring to help me, and all I could do with my Paddlers signify'd nothing, and now I began to give my self over for loſt; for as the Current was on both Sides the Island, I knew in a few Leagues Diſtance they muſt joyn again, and then I was irrecoverably gone; nor did I see any Possibility of avoiding it; so that I had no Prospeƈt before me but of Perishing; not by the Sea, for that was calm enough, but of ſtarving for Hunger. I had indeed found a Tortoise on the Shore, as big almoſt as I could lift, and had toss'd it into the Boat; and I had a great Jar of fresh Water, that is to say, one of my Earthen Pots; but what was all this to being driven into the vaſt Ocean, where to be sure, there was no Shore, no main Land, or Island, for a thousand Leagues at leaſt.

And now I saw how easy it was for the Providence of
God to make the moſt miserable Condition Mankind
could be in *worse*. Now I look'd back upon my desolate
solitary Island, as the moſt pleasant Place in the World,
and all the Happiness my Heart could wish for, was to be
but there again. I ſtretch'd out my Hands to it with eager
Wishes. O happy Desart, said I, I shall never see thee
more. O miserable Creature, said I, whether am I going:
Then I reproach'd my self with my unthankful Temper,
and how I had repin'd at my solitary Condition; and now
what would I give to be on Shore there again. Thus we
never see the true State of our Condition, till it is illus-
trated to us by its Contraries; nor know how to value
what we enjoy, but by the want of it. It is scarce possible
to imagine the Conſternation I was now in, being driven
from my beloved Island (for so it appear'd to me now to
be) into the wide Ocean, almoſt two Leagues, and in the
utmoſt Despair of ever recovering it again. However, I
work'd hard, till indeed my Strength was almoſt exhauſted, and kept my Boat as much to the *Northward*, that is,
towards the Side of the Current which the Eddy lay on,
as possibly I could; when about Noon, as the Sun pass'd
the Meridian, I thought I felt a little Breeze of Wind in
my Face, springing up from the *S. S. E.* This chear'd my
Heart a little, and especially when in about half an Hour
more, it blew a pretty small gentle Gale. By this Time I
was gotten at a frightful Diſtance from the Island, and
had the leaſt Cloud of haizy Weather interven'd, I had
been undone another Way too; for I had no Compass on
Board, and should never have known how to have ſteer'd
towards the Island, if I had but once loſt Sight of it;
but the Weather continuing clear, I apply'd my self to
get up my Maſt again, spread my Sail, ſtanding away

to the *North*, as much as possible, to get out of the Current.

Juſt as I had set my Maſt and Sail, and the Boat began to ſtretch away, I saw even by the Clearness of the Water, some Alteration of the Current was near; for where the Current was so ſtrong, the Water was foul; but perceiving the Water clear, I found the Current abate, and presently I found to the *Eaſt*, at about half a Mile, a Breach of the Sea upon some Rocks; these Rocks I found caus'd the Current to part again, and as the main Stress of it ran away more *Southerly*, leaving the Rocks to the *North-Eaſt*; so the other return'd by the Repulse of the Rocks, and made a ſtrong Eddy, which run back again to the *North-Weſt*, with a very sharp Stream.

They who know what it is to have a Reprieve brought to them upon the Ladder, or to be rescued from Thieves juſt a going to murther them, or, who have been in such like Extremities, may guess what my present Surprise of Joy was, and how gladly I put my Boat into the Stream of this Eddy, and the Wind also freshning, how gladly I spread my Sail to it, running chearfully before the Wind, and with a ſtrong Tide or Eddy under Foot.

This Eddy carryed me about a League in my Way back again directly towards the Island, but about two Leagues more to the Northward than the Current which carried me away at firſt; so that when I came near the Island, I found my self open to the Northern Shore of it, that is to say, the other End of the Island opposite to that which I went out from.

When I had made something more than a League of Way by the help of this Current or Eddy, I found it was spent and serv'd me no farther. However, I found that being between the two great Currents, (*viz.*) that on he

South Side which had hurried me away, and that on the
North which lay about a League on the other Side: I say
between these two, in the wake of the Island, I found the
Water at leaſt ſtill and running no Way, and having ſtill
a Breeze of Wind fair for me, I kept on ſteering directly
for the Island, tho' not making such fresh Way as I did
before.

About four a-Clock in the Evening, being then within
about a League of the Island, I found the Point of the
Rocks which occasioned this Disaſter, ſtretching out as
is describ'd before to the South-ward, and caſting off the
Current more Southwardly, had of Course made another
Eddy to the North, and this I found very ſtrong, but not
directly setting the Way my Course lay which was due
Weſt, but almoſt full North. However having a fresh
Gale, I ſtretch'd a-cross this Eddy slanting North-weſt,
and in about an Hour came within about a Mile of the
Shore, where it being smooth Water, I soon got to Land.

When I was on Shore I fell on my Knees and gave God
Thanks for my Deliverance, resolving to lay aside all
Thoughts of my Deliverance by my Boat, and refreshing
my self with such Things as I had, I brought my Boat
close to the Shore in a little Cove that I had spy'd under
some Trees, and lay'd me down to sleep, being quite
spent with the Labour and Fatigue of the Voyage.

I was now at a great Loss which Way to get Home with
my Boat, I had run so much Hazard, and knew too much
the Case to think of attempting it by the Way I went out,
and what might be at the other Side (I mean the Weſt
Side) I knew not, nor had I any Mind to run any more
Ventures; so I only resolved in the Morning to make my
Way Weſtward along the Shore and to see if there was no
Creek where I might lay up my Frigate in Safety, so as to

have her again if I wanted her; in about three Mile or thereabout coaſting the Shore, I came to a very good Inlet or Bay about a Mile over, which narrowed till it came to a very little Rivulet or Brook, where I found a very convenient Harbour for my Boat and where she lay as if she had been in a little Dock made on Purpose for her. Here I put in, and having ſtow'd my Boat very safe, I went on Shore to look about me and see where I was.

I soon found I had but a little paſt by the Place where I had been before, when I travell'd on Foot to that Shore; so taking nothing out of my Boat, but my Gun and my Umbrella, for it was exceeding hot, I began my March: The Way was comfortable enough after such a Voyage as I had been upon, and I reach'd my old Bower in the Evening, where I found every thing ſtanding as I left it; for I always kept it in good Order, being, as I said before, my Country House.

I got over the Fence, and laid me down in the Shade to reſt my Limbs; for I was very weary, and fell asleep: But judge you, if you can, that read my Story, what a Surprize I muſt be in, when I was wak'd out of my Sleep by a Voice calling me by my Name several times, *Robin, Robin, Robin Crusoe,* poor *Robin Crusoe,* where are you *Robin Crusoe?* Where are you? Where have you been?

I was so dead asleep at firſt, being fatigu'd with Rowing, or Paddling, as it is call'd, the firſt Part of the Day, and with walking the latter Part, that I did not wake thoroughly, but dozing between sleeping and waking, thought I dream'd that some Body spoke to me: But as the Voice continu'd to repeat *Robin Crusoe, Robin Crusoe,* at laſt I began to wake more perfeƈtly, and was at firſt dreadfully frighted, and ſtarted up in the utmoſt Conſternation: But no sooner were my Eyes open, than I

saw my *Poll* sitting on the Top of the Hedge; and immediately knew that it was he that spoke to me; for juſt
in such bemoaning Language I had used to talk to him,
and teach him; and he had learn'd it so perfeᶜtly, that he
would sit upon my Finger, and lay his Bill close to my
Face, and cry, *Poor* Robin Crusoe, *Where are you? Where
have you been? How come you here?* And such things as I
had taught him.

However, even though I knew it was the Parrot, and
that indeed it could be no Body else, it was a good while
before I could compose my self: Firſt, I was amazed how
the Creature got thither, and then, how he should juſt
keep about the Place, and no where else: But as I was well
satisfied it could be no Body but honeſt *Poll*, I got it over;
and holding out my Hand, and calling him by his Name
Poll, the sociable Creature came to me, and sat upon my
Thumb, as he used to do, and continu'd talking to me,
Poor Robin Crusoe, and *how did I come here?* and *where
had I been?* juſt as if he had been overjoy'd to see me
again; and so I carry'd him Home along with me.

I had now had enough of rambling to Sea for some
time, and had enough to do for many Days to sit ſtill, and
refleᶜt upon the Danger I had been in: I would have been
very glad to have had my Boat again on my Side of the Island; but I knew not how it was praᶜticable to get it
about. As to the Eaſt Side of the Island, which I had gone
round; I knew well enough there was no venturing that
Way; my very heart would shrink, and my very Blood
run chill but to think of it: And as to the other Side of the
Island, I did not know how it might be there; but supposing the Current ran with the same Force againſt the
Shore at the Eaſt as it pass'd by it on the other, I might
run the same Risk of being driven down the Stream, and

carry'd by the Island, as I had been before, of being carry'd away from it; so with these Thoughts I contented
my self to be without any Boat, though it had been the
Product of so many Months Labour to make it, and of so
many more to get it unto the Sea.

In this Government of my Temper, I remain'd near a
Year, liv'd a very sedate retir'd Life, as you may well suppose; and my Thoughts being very much composed as to
my Condition, and fully comforted in resigning my self
to the Dispositions of Providence, I thought I liv'd
really very happily in all things, except that of Society.

I improv'd my self in this time in all the mechanick
Exercises which my Necessities put me upon applying
my self to, and I believe cou'd, upon Occasion, make a
very good *Carpenter,* especially considering how few
Tools I had.

Besides this, I arriv'd at an unexpected Perfection in
my Earthen Ware, and contriv'd well enough to make
them with a Wheel, which I found infinitely easyer and
better; because I made things round and shapable, which
before were filthy things indeed to look on. But I think I
was never more vain of my own Performance, or more
joyful for any thing I found out, than for my being able to
make a Tobacco-Pipe. And tho' it was a very ugly clumsy
thing, when it was done, and only burnt red like other
Earthen Ware, yet as it was hard and firm, and would
draw the Smoke, I was exceedingly comforted with it,
for I had been always used to smoke, and there were Pipes
in the Ship, but I forgot them at first, not knowing that
there was Tobacco in the Island; and afterwards, when
I search'd the Ship again, I could not come at any Pipes
at all.

In my Wicker Ware also I improved much, and made

abundance of necessary Baskets, as well as my Invention
shew'd me, tho' not very handsome, yet they were such
as were very handy and convenient for my laying things
up in, or fetching things home in. For Example, if I
kill'd a Goat abroad, I could hang it up in a Tree, flea it,
and dress it, and cut it in Pieces, and bring it home in a
Basket, and the like by a Turtle, I could cut it up, take
out the Eggs, and a Piece or two of the Flesh, which was
enough for me, and bring them home in a Basket, and
leave the reſt behind me. Also large deep Baskets were
my Receivers for my Corn, which I always rubb'd out as
soon as it was dry, and cured, and kept it in great Baskets.

I began now to perceive my Powder abated considerably, and this was a Want which it was impossible for me
to supply, and I began seriously to consider what I muſt
do when I should have no more Powder; that is to say,
how I should do to kill any Goat. I had, as is observ'd in
the third Year of my being here, kept a young Kid, and
bred her up tame, and I was in hope of getting a He-
Goat, but I could not by any Means bring it to pass, 'till
my Kid grew an old Goat; and I could never find it my
Heart to kill her, till she dy'd at laſt of meer Age.

But being now in the eleventh Year of my Residence
and, as I have said, my Ammunition growing low, I set
my self to ſtudy some Art to trap and snare the Goats, to
see whether I could not catch some of them alive, and
particularly I wanted a She-Goat great with young.

To this Purpose I made Snares to hamper them, and I
do believe they were more than once taken in them, but
my Tackle was not good, for I had no Wire, and I always
found them broken, and my Bait devoured.

At length I resolv'd to try a Pit-Fall, so I dug several
large Pits in the Earth, in Places where I had observ'd

the Goats used to feed, and over these Pits I plac'd Hurdles of my own making too, with a great Weight upon them; and several times I put Ears of Barley, and dry Rice, without setting the Trap, and I could easily perceive that the Goats had gone in and eaten up the Corn, for I could see the Mark of their Feet. At length I set three Traps in one Night, and going the next Morning I found them all standing, and yet the Bait eaten and gone: This was very discouraging. However, I alter'd my Trap, and, not to trouble you with Particulars, going one Morning to see my Trap, I found in one of them a large old He-Goat, and in one of the other, three Kids, a Male and two Females.

As to the old one, I knew not what to do with him, he was so fierce I durst not go into the Pit to him; that is to say, to go about to bring him away alive, which was what I wanted. I could have kill'd him, but that was not my Business, nor would it answer my End. So I e'en let him out, and he ran away as if he had been frighted out of his Wits: but I had forgot then what I learn'd afterwards, that Hunger will tame a Lyon. If I had let him stay there three or four Days without Food, and then have carry'd him some Water to drink, and then a little Corn, he would have been as tame as one of the Kids, for they are mighty sagacious tractable Creatures where they are well used.

However, for the present I let him go, knowing no better at that time; then I went to the three Kids, and taking them one by one, I tyed them with Strings together, and with some Difficulty brought them all home.

It was a good while before they wou'd feed, but throwing them some sweet Corn, it tempted them and they began to be tame; and now I found that if I expected to supply my self with Goat-Flesh when I had no Powder or Shot left, breeding some up tame was my only way, when perhaps I might have them about my House like a Flock of Sheep.

But then it presently occurr'd to me, that I must keep the tame from the wild, or else they would always run wild when they grew up, and the only Way for this was to have some enclosed Piece of Ground, well fenc'd either with Hedge or Pale, to keep them in so effectually, that those within might not break out, or those without break in.

This was a great Undertaking for one Pair of Hands, yet as I saw there was an absolute Necessity of doing it, my first Piece of Work was to find out a proper Piece of Ground, *viz.* where there was likely to be Herbage for them to eat, Water for them to drink, and Cover to keep them from the Sun.

Those who understand such Enclosures will think I had very little Contrivance, when I pitch'd upon a Place very proper for all these, being a plain open Piece of Meadow-Land, or *Savanna*, (as our People call it in the Western Collonies,) which had two or three little Drills of fresh Water in it, and at one end was very woody. I say they will smile at my Forecast, when I shall tell them I began my enclosing of this Piece of Ground in such a manner, that my Hedge or Pale must have been at least two Mile about. Nor was the Madness of it so great as to the Compass, for if it was ten Mile about I was like to have time enough to do it in. But I did not consider that my Goats would be as wild in so much Compass as if they had had the whole Island, and I should have so much Room to chace them in, that I should never catch them.

My Hedge was begun and carry'd on, I believe, about

fifty Yards, when this Thought occurr'd to me, so I presently stopt short, and for the first beginning I resolv'd to enclose a Piece of about 150 Yards in length, and 100 Yards in breadth, which as it would maintain as many as I should have in any reasonable time, so as my Flock encreased, I could add more Ground to my Enclosure.

This was acting with some Prudence, and I went to work with Courage. I was about three Months hedging in the first Piece, and till I had done it I tether'd the three Kids in the best part of it, and us'd them to feed as near me as possible to make them familiar; and very often I would go and carry them some Ears of Barley, or a handful of Rice, and feed them out of my Hand; so that after my Enclosure was finished, and I let them loose, they would follow me up and down, bleating after me for a handful of Corn.

This answer'd my End, and in about a Year and half I had a Flock of about twelve Goats, Kids and all; and in two Years more I had three and forty, besides several that I took and kill'd for my Food. And after that I enclosed five several Pieces of Ground to feed them in, with little Pens to drive them into, to take them as I wanted, and Gates out of one Piece of Ground into another.

But this was not all, for now I not only had Goats Flesh to feed on when I pleas'd, but Milk too, a thing which indeed in my beginning I did not so much as think of, and which, when it came into my Thoughts, was really an agreeable Surprize. For now I set up my Dairy, and had sometimes a Gallon or two of Milk in a Day. And as Nature, who gives Supplies of Food to every Creature, dictates even naturally how to make use of it; so I that had never milk'd a Cow, much less a Goat, or seen Butter or Cheese made, very readily and handily, tho' after a great many Essays and Miscarriages, made me both Butter and Cheese at laſt, and never wanted it afterwards.

How mercifully can our great Creator treat his Creatures, even in those Conditions in which they seem'd to be overwhelm'd in Deſtruction. How can he sweeten the bittereſt Providences, and give us Cause to praise him for Dungeons and Prisons. What a Table was here spread for me in a Wilderness, where I saw nothing at firſt but to perish for Hunger.

It would have made a Stoick smile to have seen, me and my little Family sit down to Dinner; there was my Majeſty the Prince and Lord of the whole Island; I had the Lives of all my Subjects at my absolute Command. I could hang, draw, give Liberty, and take it away, and no Rebels among all my Subjects.

Then to see how like a King I din'd too all alone, attended by my Servants, *Poll,* as if he had been my Favourite, was the only Person permitted to talk to me. My Dog who was now grown very old and crazy, and had found no Species to multiply his Kind upon, sat always at my Right Hand, and two Cats, one on one Side the Table, and one on the other, expecting now and then a Bit from my Hand, as a Mark of special Favour.

But these were not the two Cats which I brought on Shore at firſt, for they were both of them dead, and had been interr'd near my Habitation by my own Hand; but one of them having multiply'd by I know not what Kind of Creature, these were two which I had preserv'd tame, whereas the reſt run wild in the Woods, and became indeed troublesom to me at laſt; for they would often come into my House, and plunder me too, till at laſt I was obliged to shoot them, and did kill a great many; at length they left me: With this Attendance, and in this plentiful

Manner I lived; neither could I be said to want any thing but Society, and of that in some time after this, I was like to have too much.

I was something impatient, as I have observ'd, to have the Use of my Boat; though very loath to run any more Hazards; and therefore sometimes I sat contriving Ways to get her about the Island, and at other Times I sat my self down contented enough without her. But I had a ſtrange Uneasiness in my Mind to go down to the Point of the Island, where, as I have said, in my laſt Ramble, I went up the Hill to see how the Shore lay, and how the Current set, that I might see what I had to do: This Inclination encreas'd upon me every Day, and at length I resolv'd to travel thither by Land, following the Edge of the Shore. I did so: But had any one in *England* been to meet such a Man as I was, it muſt either have frighted them, or rais'd a great deal of Laughter; and as I frequently ſtood ſtill to look at my self, I could not but smile at the Notion of my travelling through *Yorkshire* with such an Equipage, and in such a Dress: Be pleas'd to take a Sketch of my Figure as follows.

I had a great high shapeless Cap, made of a Goat's Skin, with a Flap hanging down behind, as well to keep the Sun from me, as to shoot the Rain off from running into my Neck; nothing being so hurtful in these Climates, as the Rain upon the Flesh under the Cloaths.

I had a short Jacket of Goat-Skin, the Skirts coming down to about the middle of my Thighs; and a Pair of open-knee'd Breeches of the same, the Breeches were made of the Skin of an old *He-goat*, whose Hair hung down such a Length on either Side, that like *Pantaloons* it reach'd to the middle of my Legs; Stockings and Shoes I had none, but had made me a Pair of some-things, I

scarce know what to call them, like Buskins to flap over
my Legs, and lace on either Side like Spatter-dashes; but
of a moſt barbarous Shape, as indeed were all the reſt of
my Cloaths.

I had on a broad Belt of Goat's-Skin dry'd, which I
drew together with two Thongs of the same, inſtead of
Buckles, and in a kind of a Frog on either Side of this. Inſtead of a Sword and a Dagger, hung a little Saw and a
Hatchet, one on one Side, one on the other. I had another
Belt not so broad, and faſten'd in the same Manner, which
hung over my Shoulder; and at the End of it, under my
left Arm, hung two Pouches, both made of Goat's-Skin
too; in one of which hung my Powder, in the other my
Shot: At my Back I carry'd my Basket, on my Shoulder
my Gun, and over my Head a great clumsy ugly Goat-
Skin Umbrella, but which, after all, was the moſt necessary Thing I had about me, next to my Gun: As for my
Face, the Colour of it was really not so *Moletta*, like as one
might expeƈt from a Man not at all careful of it, and living within nine or ten Degrees of the *Equinox*. My Beard
I had once suffer'd to grow till it was about a Quarter of a
Yard long; but as I had both Scissars and Razors sufficient, I had cut it pretty short, except what grew on my
upper Lip, which I had trimm'd into a large Pair of *Ma-
hometan* Whiskers, such as I had seen worn by some
Turks, who I saw at *Sallee*; for the *Moors* did not wear
such, tho' the *Turks* did; of these Muſtachioes or Whiskers, I will not say they were long enough to hang my
Hat upon them; but they were of a Length and Shape
monſtrous enough, and such as in *England* would have
pass'd for frightful.

But all this is by the by; for as to my Figure, I had so
few to observe me, that it was of no manner of Conse-

quence; so I say no more to that Part. In this kind of
Figure I went my new Journey, and was out five or six
Days. I travell'd firſt along the Sea Shore, directly to the
Place where I firſt brought my Boat to an Anchor, to get
up upon the Rocks; and having no Boat now to take care
of, I went over the Land a nearer Way to the sameHeight
that I was upon before, when looking forward to the
Point of the Rocks which lay out, and which I was oblig'd to double with my Boat, as is said above: I was surpriz'd to see the Sea all smooth and quiet, no Ripling, no
Motion, no Current, any more there than in other Places.

I was at a ſtrange Loss to underſtand this, and resolv'd
to spend some Time in the observing it, to see if nothing
from the Sets of the Tide had occasion'd it; but I was
presently convinc'd how it was, *viz.* That the Tide of
Ebb setting from the *Weſt*, and joyning with the Current
of Waters from some great river on the Shore, muſt be
the Occasion of this Current; and that according as the
Wind blew more forcibly from the *Weſt*, or from the
North, this Current came nearer, or went farther from the
Shore; for waiting thereabouts till Evening, I went up to
the Rock again, and then the Tide of Ebb being made, I
plainly saw the Current again as before, only, that it run
farther of, being near half a League from the Shore;
whereas in my Case, it set close upon the Shore, and hurry'd me and my *Canoe* along with it, which at another
Time it would not have done.

This Observation convinc'd me, That I had nothing
to do but to observe the Ebbing and the Flowing of the
Tide, and I might very easily bring my Boat about the
Island again: But when I began to think of putting it in
Practice, I had such a Terror upon my Spirits at the Re-
membrance of the Danger I had been in, that I could not

think of it again with any Patience; but on the contrary, I took up another Resolution which was more safe, though more laborious; and this was, That I would build, or rather make me another *Periagua* or *Canoe*; and so have one for one Side of the Island, and one for the other.

You are to understand, that now I had, as I may call it, two Plantations in the Island; one my little Fortification or Tent, with the Wall about it under the Rock, with the Cave behind me, which by this Time I had enlarg'd into several Apartments, or Caves, one within another. One of these, which was the dryest, and largest, and had a Door out beyond my Wall or Fortification; that is to say, beyond where my Wall joyn'd to the Rock, was all fill'd up with the large Earthen Pots, of which I have given an Account, and with fourteen or fifteen great Baskets, which would hold five or six Bushels each, where I laid up my Stores of Provision, especially my Corn, some in the Ear cut off short from the Straw, and the other rubb'd out with my Hand.

As for my Wall made, *as before*, with long Stakes or Piles, those Piles grew all like Trees, and were by this Time grown so big, and spread so very much, that there was not the least Appearance to any one's View of any Habitation behind them.

Near this Dwelling of mine, but a little farther within the Land, and upon lower Ground, lay my two Pieces of Corn-Ground, which I kept duly cultivated and sow'd, and which duly yielded me their Harvest in its Season; and whenever I had occasion for more Corn, I had more Land adjoyning as fit as that.

Besides this, I had my Country Seat, and I had now a tollerable Plantation there also; for first, I had my little Bower, as I call'd it, which I kept in Repair; *that is to say,*

I kept the Hedge which circled it in, conſtantly fitted up
to its usual Height, the Ladder ſtanding always in the
Inside; I kept the Trees which at firſt were no more than
my Stakes, but were now grown very firm and tall; I kept
them always so cut, that they might spread and grow
thick and wild, and make the more agreeable Shade,
which they did effeƈtually to my Mind. In the Middle of
this I had my Tent always ſtanding, being a piece of a
Sail spread over Poles set up for that Purpose, and which
never wanted any Repair or Renewing; and under this I
had made me a Squab or Couch, with the Skins of the
Creatures I had kill'd, and with other soft Things, and a
Blanket laid on them, such as belong'd to our Sea-Bed-
ding, which I had saved, and a great Watch-Coat to cover
me; and here, whenever I had Occasion to be absent from
my chief Seat, I took up my Country Habitation.

Adjoyning to this I had my Enclosures for my Cattle,
that is to say, my Goats: And as I had taken an incon-
ceivable deal of Pains to fence and enclose this Ground,
so I was so uneasy to see it kept entire, leſt the Goats
should break thro', that I never left off till with infinite
Labour I had ſtuck the Out-side of the Hedge so full of
small Stakes, and so near to one another, that it was rather
a Pale than a Hedge, and there was scarce Room to put a
Hand thro' between them, which afterwards when those
Stakes grew, as they all did in the next rainy Season,
made the Enclosure ſtrong like a Wall, indeed ſtronger
than any Wall.

This will teſtify for me that I was not idle, and that I
spared no Pains to bring to pass whatever appear'd necessary for my comfortable Support; for I consider'd the
keeping up a Breed of tame Creatures thus at my Hand,
would be a living Magazine of Flesh, Milk, Butter and

Cheese, for me as long as I liv'd in the Place, if it were to be forty Years; and that keeping them in my Reach, depended entirely upon my perfecting my Enclosures to such a Degree, that I might be sure of keeping them together; which by this Method indeed I so effectually secur'd that, when these little Stakes began to grow, I had planted them so very thick, I was forced to pull some of them up again.

In this Place also I had my Grapes growing, which I principally depended on for my Winter Store of Raisins; and which I never fail'd to preserve very carefully, as the beſt and moſt agreeable Dainty of my whole Diet; and indeed they were not agreeable only, but physical, wholesome, nourishing, and refreshing to the laſt Degree.

As this was also about half Way between my other Habitation, and the Place where I had laid up my Boat, I generally ſtay'd, and lay here in my Way thither; for I used frequently to visit my Boat, and I kept all Things about or belonging to her in very good Order; sometimes I went out in her to divert my self, but no more hazardous Voyages would I go, nor scarce ever above a Stone's Caſt or two from the Shore, I was so apprehensive of being hurry'd out of my Knowledge again by the Currents, or Winds, or any other Accident. But now I come to a new Scene of my Life.

It happen'd one Day about Noon going towards my Boat, I was exceedingly surpriz'd with the Print of a Man's naked Foot on the Shore, which was very plain to be seen in the Sand: I ſtood like one Thunder-ſtruck, or as if I had seen an Apparition; I liſten'd, I look'd round me, I could hear nothing, nor see any Thing; I went up to a rising Ground to look farther; I went up the Shore and down the Shore, but it was all one, I could see no other Impression but that one, I went to it again to see if there were any more, and to observe if it might not be my Fancy; but there was no Room for that, for there was exactly the very Print of a Foot, Toes, Heel, and every Part of a Foot; how it came thither, I knew not, nor could in the least imagine. But after innumerable fluttering Thoughts, like a Man perfectly confus'd and out of my self, I came Home to my Fortification, not feeling, as we say, the Ground I went on, but terrify'd to the last Degree, looking behind me at every two or three Steps, mistaking every Bush and Tree, and fancying every Stump at a Distance to be a Man; nor is it possible to describe how many various Shapes affrighted Imagination represented Things to me in, how many wild Ideas were found every Moment in my Fancy, and what strange unaccountable Whimsies came into my Thoughts by the Way.

When I came to my Castle, for so I think I call'd it ever after this, I fled into it like one pursued; whether I went over by the Ladder as first contriv'd, or went in at the Hole in the Rock, which I call'd a Door, I cannot remember; no, nor could I remember the next Morning, for never frighted Hare fled to Cover, or Fox to Earth, with more Terror of Mind than I to this Retreat.

I slept none that Night; the farther I was from the Occasion of my Fright, the greater my Apprehensions were, which is something contrary to the Nature of such Things, and especially to the usual Practice of all Creatures in Fear: But I was so embarrass'd with my own frightful Ideas of the Thing, that I form'd nothing but dismal Imaginations to my self, even tho' I was now a great way off of it. Sometimes I fancy'd it must be the Devil; and Reason joyn'd in with me upon this Supposition: For how should any other Thing in human Shape come into the Place? Where was the Vessel that brought them? What Marks was there of any other Footsteps! And how was it possible a Man should come there? But then to think that *Satan* should take human Shape upon him in such a Place where there could be no manner of Occasion for it, but to leave the Print of his Foot behind him, and that even for no Purpose too, for he could not be sure I should see it; this was an Amusement the other Way; I consider'd that the Devil might have found out abundance of other Ways to have terrify'd me than this of the single Print of a Foot. That as I liv'd quite on the other Side of the Island, he would never have been so simple to leave a Mark in a Place where 'twas Ten Thousand to one whether I should ever see it or not, and in the Sand too, which the first Surge of the Sea upon a high Wind would have defac'd entirely: All this seem'd inconsistent with the Thing it self, and with all the Notions we usually entertain of the Subtilty of the Devil.

Abundance of such Things as these assisted to argue me out of all Apprehensions of its being the Devil: And I presently concluded then, that it must be some more dangerous Creature, (*viz.*) That it must be some of the Savages of the main Land over-against me, who had wander'd out to Sea in their *Canoes*; and either driven by the Currents, or by contrary Winds had made the Island; and had been on Shore, but were gone away again to Sea, being as loth, perhaps, to have stay'd in this desolate Island, as I would have been to have had them.

While these Reflections were rowling upon my Mind, I was very thankful in my Thoughts, that I was so happy as not to be thereabouts at that Time, or that they did not see my Boat, by which they would have concluded that some Inhabitants had been in the Place, and perhaps have search'd farther for me: Then terrible Thoughts rack'd my Imagination about their having found my Boat, and that there were People here; and that if so, I should certainly have them come again in greater Numbers, and devour me; that if it should happen so that they should not find me, yet they would find my Enclosure, deſtroy all my Corn, carry away all my Flock of tame Goats, and I should perish at laſt for meer Want.

Thus my Fear banish'd all my religious Hope; all that former Confidence in God which was founded upon such wonderful Experience as I had had of his Goodness, now vanished, as if he that had fed me by Miracle hitherto, could not preserve by his Power the Provision which he had made for me by his Goodness: I reproach'd my self with my Easiness, that would not sow any more Corn one Year than would juſt serve me till the next Season as if no Accident could intervene to prevent my enjoying the Crop that was upon the Ground; and this I thought so juſt a Reproof, that I resolv'd for the future to have two or three Years Corn beforehand, so that whatever might come, I might not perish for want of Bread.

How ſtrange a Chequer Work of Providence is the Life of Man! and by what secret differing Springs are the Affeꝗions hurry'd about as differing Circumſtances present! To Day we love what to Morrow we hate; to Day we seek what to Morrow we shun; to Day we desire what to Morrow we fear; nay even tremble at the Apprehensions of; this was exemplify'd in me at this Time in the moſt lively Manner imaginable; for I whose only Affliction was, that I seem'd banished from human Society, that I was alone, circumscrib'd by the boundless Ocean, cut off from Mankind, and condemn'd to what I call'd silent Life; that I was as one who Heaven thought not worthy to be number'd among the Living, or to appear among the rest of his Creatures; that to have seen one of my own Species, would have seem'd to me a Raising me from Death to Life, and the greatest Blessing that Heaven it self, next to the supreme Blessing of Salvation, could bestow; *I say*, that I should now tremble at the very Apprehensions of seeing a Man, and was ready to sink into the Ground at but the Shadow or silent Appearance of a Man's having set his Foot in the Island.

Such is the uneven State of human Life: And it afforded me a great many curious Speculations afterwards, when I had a little recover'd my first Surprize; I consider'd that this was the Station of Life the infinitely wise and good Providence of God had determin'd for me, that as I could not foresee what the Ends of Divine Wisdom might be in all this, so I was not to dispute his Sovereignty, who, as I was his Creature, had an undoubted Right by Creation to govern and dispose of me absolutely as he thought fit; and who, as I was a Creature who had offended him, had likewise a judicial Right to condemn me to what Punishment he thought fit; and that it was my Part to submit to bear his Indignation, because I had sinn'd against him.

I then reflected that God, who was not only Righteous but Omnipotent, as he had thought fit thus to punish and afflict me, so he was able to deliver me; that if he did not think fit to do it, 'twas my unquestion'd Duty to resign my self absolutely and entirely to his Will; and on the other Hand, it was my Duty also to hope in him, pray to him, and quietly to attend the Dictates and Directions of his daily Providence.

These Thoughts took me up many Hours, Days; nay,

I may say, Weeks and Months; and one particular Effect of my Cogitations on this Occasion, I cannot omit, *viz.* One Morning early, lying in my Bed, and fill'd with Thought about my Danger from the Appearance of Savages, I found it discompos'd me very much, upon which those Words of the Scripture came into my Thoughts, *Call upon me in the Day of Trouble, and I will deliver, and thou shalt glorify me.*

Upon this, rising chearfully out of my Bed, my Heart was not only comforted, but I was guided and encourag d to pray earnestly to God for Deliverance: When I had done praying, I took up my Bible, and opening it to read, the first Words that presented to me, were, *Wait on the Lord, and be of good Cheer, and he shall strengthen thy Heart; wait, I say, on the Lord:* It is impossible to express the Comfort this gave me. In Answer, I thankfully laid down the Book, and was no more sad, at least, not on that Occasion.

In the middle of these Cogitations, Apprehensions and Reflections, it came into my Thought one Day, that all this might be a meer Chimera of my own; and that this Foot might be the Print of my own Foot, when I came on Shore from my Boat: This chear'd me up a little too, and I began to perswade my self it was all a Delusion; that it was nothing else but my own Foot, and why might not I come that way from the Boat, as well as I was going that way to the Boat; again, I consider'd also that I could by no Means tell for certain where I had trod, and where I had not; and that if at last this was only the Print of my own Foot, I had play'd the Part of those Fools, who strive to make Stories of Spectres, and Apparitions; and then are frighted at them more than any body.

Now I began to take Courage, and to peep abroad

again; for I had not ſtirr'd out of my Caſtle for three Days and Nights; so that I began to ſtarve for Provision; for I had little or nothing within Doors, but some Barley Cakes and Water. Then I knew that my Goats wanted to be milk'd too, which usually was my Evening Diversion; and the poor Creatures were in great Pain and Inconvenience for want of it; and indeed, it almoſt spoil'd some of them, and almoſt dry'd up their Milk.

Heartning my self therefore with the Belief that this was nothing but the Print of one of my own Feet, and so I might be truly said to ſtart at my own Shadow, I began to go abroad again, and went to my Country House, to milk my Flock; but to see with what Fear I went forward, how often I look'd behind me, how I was ready every now and then to lay down my Basket, and run for my Life, it would have made any one have thought I was haunted with an evil Conscience, or that I had been lately moſt terribly frighted, and so indeed I had.

However, as I went down thus two or three Days, and having seen nothing, I began to be a little bolder; and to think there was really nothing in it, but my own Imagination: But I cou'd not perswade my self fully of this, till I should go down to the Shore again, and see this Print of a Foot, and measure it by my own, and see if there was any Similitude or Fitness, that I might be assur'd it was my own Foot: But when I came to the Place, *Firſt*, It appear'd evidently to me, that when I laid up my Boat, I could not possibly be on Shore any where there about. *Secondly*, When I came to measure the Mark with my own Foot, I found my Foot not so large by a great deal; both these Things fill'd my Head with new Imaginations, and gave me the Vapours again, to the higheſt Degree; so that I shook with cold, like one in an Ague: And

I went Home again, fill'd with the Belief that some Man or Men had been on Shore there; or in short, that the Island was inhabited, and I might be surpriz'd before I was aware; and what course to take for my Security I knew not.

O what ridiculous Resolution Men take, when possess'd with Fear! It deprives them of the Use of those Means which Reason offers for their Relief. The first Thing I propos'd to my self, was, to throw down my Enclosures, and turn all my tame Cattle wild into the Woods, that the Enemy might not find them; and then frequent the Island in Prospect of the same, or the like Booty: Then to the simple Thing of Digging up my two Corn Fields, that they might not find such a Grain there, and still be prompted to frequent the Island; then to demolish my Bower, and Tent, that they might not see any Vestiges of Habitation, and be prompted to look farther, in order to find out the Persons inhabiting.

These were the Subject of the first Night's Cogitation, after I was come Home again, while the Apprehensions which had so over-run my Mind were fresh upon me, and my Head was full of Vapours, as above: Thus Fear of Danger is ten thousand Times more terrifying than Danger it self, when apparent to the Eyes; and we find the Burthen of Anxiety greater by much, than the Evil which we are anxious about; and which was worse than all this, I had not that Relief in this Trouble from the Resignation I used to practise, that I hop'd to have. I look'd, I thought, like *Saul*, who complain'd not only that the *Philistines* were upon him; but that God had forsaken him; for I did not now take due Ways to compose my Mind, by crying to God in my Distress, and resting upon his Providence, as I had done before, for my Defence and

Deliverance; which if I had done, I had, at least, been more cheerfully supported under this new Surprise, and perhaps carry'd through it with more Resolution.

This Confusion of my Thoughts kept me waking all Night; but in the Morning I fell asleep, and having by the Amusement of my Mind, been, as it were, tyr'd, and my Spirits exhausted; I slept very soundly, and wak'd much better compos'd than I had ever been before; and now I began to think sedately; and upon the utmost Debate with my self, I concluded, That this Island, which was so exceeding pleasant, fruitful, and no farther from the main Land than as I had seen, was not so entirely abandon'd as I might imagine: That altho' there were no stated Inhabitants who liv'd on the Spot; yet that there might sometimes come Boats off from the Shore, who either with Design, or perhaps never, but when they were driven by cross Winds, might come to this Place.

That I had liv'd here fifteen Years now, and had not met with the least Shadow or Figure of any People yet; and that if at any Time they should be driven here, it was probable they went away again as soon as ever they could, seeing they had never thought fit to fix there upon any Occasion, to this Time.

That the most I cou'd suggest any Danger from, was, from any such casual accidental Landing of straggling People from the Main, who, as it was likely if they were driven hither, were here against their Wills; so they made no stay here, but went off again with all possible Speed, seldom staying one Night on Shore, least they should not have the Help of the Tides, and Day-light back again; and that therefore I had nothing to do but to consider of some safe Retreat, in Case I should see any Savages land upon the Spot.

Now I began sorely to repent, that I had dug my Cave so large, as to bring a Door through again, which Door, as I said, came out beyond where my Fortification joyn'd to the Rock; upon maturely considering this therefore, I resolv'd to draw me a second Fortification, in the same Manner of a Semicircle, at a Diſtance from my Wall juſt where I had planted a double Row of Trees, about twelve Years before, of which I made mention: These Trees having been planted so thick before, they wanted but a few Piles to be driven between them, that they should be thicker, and ſtronger, and my Wall would be soon finish'd.

So that I had now a double Wall, and my outer Wall was thickned with Pieces of Timber, old Cables, and every Thing I could think of, to make it ſtrong; having in it seven little Holes, about as big as I might put my Arm out at: In the In-side of this, I thickned my Wall to above ten Foot thick, with continual bringing Earth out of my Cave, and laying it at the Foot of the Wall, and walking upon it; and through the seven Holes, I contriv'd to plant the Musquets, of which I took Notice, that I got seven on Shore out of the Ship; these, I say, I planted like my Cannon, and fitted them into Frames that held them like a Carriage, that so I could fire all the seven Guns in two Minutes Time: This Wall I was many a weary Month a finishing, and yet never thought my self safe till it was done.

When this was done, I ſtuck all the Ground without my Wall, for a great way every way, as full with Stakes or Sticks of the *Osier* like Wood, which I found so apt to grow, as they could well ſtand; insomuch, that I believe I might set in near twenty thousand of them, leaving a pretty large Space between them and my Wall, that I might have room to see an Enemy, and they might have no shelter from the young Trees, if they attempted to approach my outer Wall.

Thus in two Years Time I had a thick Grove and in five or six Years Time I had a Wood before my Dwelling, growing so monſtrous thick and ſtrong, that it was indeed perfeƈtly impassable; and no Men of what kind soever, would ever imagine that there was any Thing beyond it, much less a Habitation: As for the Way which I propos'd to my self to go in and out, for I left no Avenue, it was by setting two Ladders, one to a Part of the Rock which was low, and then broke in, and left room to place another Ladder upon that; so when the two Ladders were taken down, no Man living could come down to me without mischieving himself; and if they had come down they were ſtill on the Out-side of my outer Wall.

Thus I took all the Measures humane Prudence could suggeſt for my own Preservation; and it will be seen at length, that they were not altogether without juſt Reason; though I foresaw nothing at that Time, more than my meer Fear suggeſted to me.

While this was doing, I was not altogether Careless of my other Affairs; for I had a great Concern upon me, for my little Herd of Goats; they were not only a present Supply to me upon every Occasion, and began to be sufficient to me, without the Expence of Powder and Shot; but also without the Fatigue of Hunting after the wild Ones, and I was loth to lose the Advantage of them, and to have them all to nurse up over again.

To this Purpose, after long Consideration, I could think of but two Ways to preserve them; one was to find another convenient Place to dig a Cave Under-ground, and to drive them into it every Night; and the other was to enclose two or three little Bits of Land, remote from one another and as much conceal'd as I could, where I might keep about half a Dozen young Goats in each Place: So that if any Disaſter happen'd to the Flock in general, I might be able to raise them again with little Trouble and Time: And this, tho' it would require a great deal of Time and Labour, I thought was the moſt rational Design.

Accordingly I spent some Time to find out the moſt retir'd Parts of the Island; and I pitch'd upon one which was as private indeed as my Heart could wish for; it was a little damp Piece of Ground in the Middle of the hollow and thick Woods, where, as is observ'd, I almoſt loſt my self once before, endeavouring to come back that Way from the Eaſtern Part of the Island: Here I found a clear Piece of Land near three Acres, so surrounded with Woods, that it was almoſt an Enclosure by Nature, at leaſt it did not want near so much Labour to make it so, as the other Pieces of Ground I had work'd so hard at.

I immediately went to Work with this Piece of Ground, and in less than a Month's Time, I had so fenc'd it round, that my Flock or Herd, call it which you please, who were not so wild now as at firſt they might be supposed to be, were well enough secur'd in it. So, without any farther Delay, I removed ten young She-Goats and two He-Goats to this Piece; and when they were there, I continued to perfeċt the Fence till I had made it as secure as the other, which, however, I did at more Leisure, and it took me up more Time by a great deal.

All this Labour I was at the Expence of, purely from my Apprehensions on the Account of the Print of a Man's Foot which I had seen; for as yet I never saw any human Creature come near the Island, and I had now

liv'd two Years under these Uneasinesses, which indeed
made my Life much less comfortable than it was before;
as may well be imagin'd by any who know what it is to
live in the constant Snare of *the Fear of Man*; and this I
must observe with Grief too, that the Discomposure of
my Mind had too great impressions also upon the religious Part of my Thoughts, for the Dread and Terror of
falling into the Hands of Savages and Canibals, lay so
upon my Spirits, that I seldom found my self in a due
Temper for application to my Maker, at least not with
the sedate Calmness and Resignation of Soul which I was
wont to do; I rather pray'd to God as under great Affliction and Pressure of Mind, surrounded with Danger, and
in Expectation every Night of being murther'd and devour'd before Morning; and I must testify from my Experience, that a Temper of Peace, Thankfulness, Love
and Affection, is much more the proper Frame for Prayer
than that of Terror and Discomposure; and that under
the Dread of Mischief impending, a Man is no more fit
for a comforting Performance of the Duty of praying to
God, than he is for Repentance on a sick Bed: For these
Discomposures affect the Mind as the others do the Body; and the Discomposure of the Mind must necessarily
be as great a Disability as that of the Body, and much
greater, Praying to God being properly an Act of the
Mind, not of the Body.

But to go on; After I had thus secur'd one Part of my
little living Stock, I went about the whole Island, searching for another private Place, to make such another De-
posit; when wandring more to the *West* Point of the Island, than I had ever gone yet, and looking out to Sea, I
thought I saw a Boat upon the Sea, at a great Distance; I
had found a Prospective Glass, or two, in one of the Sea-

men's Chests, which I sav'd out of our Ship; but I had it not about me, and this was so remote, that I could not tell what to make of it; though I look'd at it till my eyes were not able to hold to look any longer; whether it was a Boat, or not, I do not know; but as I descended from the Hill, I could see no more of it, so I gave it over; only I resolv'd to go no more out without a Prospective Glass in my Pocket.

When I was come down the Hill, to the End of the Island, where indeed, I had never been before, I was presently convinc'd, that the seeing the Print of a Man's Foot, was not such a strange Thing in the Island as I imagin'd; and but that it was a special Providence that I was cast upon the Side of the Island, where the Savages never came: I should easily have known, that nothing was more frequent than for the *Canoes* from the Main, when they happen'd to be a little too far out at Sea, to shoot over to that Side of the Island for Harbour; likewise as they often met, and fought in their *Canoes*, the Victors having taken any Prisoners, would bring them over to this Shore, where according to their dreadful Customs, being all *Canibals*, they would kill and eat them; of which hereafter.

When I was come down the Hill, to the Shore, as I said above, being the *S. W.* Point of the Island, I was perfectly confounded and amaz'd; nor is it possible for me to express the Horror of my Mind, at seeing the Shore spread with Skulls, Hands, Feet, and other Bones of humane Bodies; and particularly I observ'd a Place where there had been a Fire made, and a Circle dug in the Earth, like a Cockpit, where it is suppos'd the Savage Wretches had sat down to their inhumane Feastings upon the Bodies of their Fellow-Creatures.

I was so astonish'd with the Sight of these Things, that I entertain'd no Notions of any Danger to my self from it for a long while; All my Apprehensions were bury'd in the Thoughts of such a Pitch of inhuman, hellish Brutality, and the Horror of the Degeneracy of Humane Nature; which though I had heard of often, yet I never had so near a View of before; in short, I turn'd away my Face from the horrid Spectacle; my Stomach grew sick, and I was just at the Point of Fainting, when Nature discharg'd the Disorder from my Stomach, and having vomited with an uncommon Violence, I was a little reliev'd; but cou'd not bear to stay in the Place a Moment; so I gat me up the Hill again, with all the Speed I cou'd, and walk'd on towards my own Habitation.

When I came a little out of that Part of the Island, I stood still a while as amaz'd; and then recovering my self, I looked up with the utmost Affection of my Soul, and with a Flood of Tears in my Eyes, gave God Thanks that had cast my first Lot in a Part of the World, where I was distinguish'd from such dreadful Creatures as these; and that though I had esteem'd my present Condition very miserable, had yet given me so many Comforts in it, that I had still more to give Thanks for than to complain of; and this above all, that I had even in this miserable Condition been comforted with the Knowledge of himself, and the Hope of his Blessing, which was a Felicity more than sufficiently equivalent to all the Misery which I had suffer'd, or could suffer.

In this Frame of Thankfulness, I went Home to my Castle, and began to be much easier now, as to the Safety of my Circumstances, than ever I was before; for I observ'd, that these Wretches never came to this Island in search of what they could get; perhaps not seeking, not wanting, or not expecting any Thing here; and having often, no doubt, been up in the cover'd woody Part of it, without finding any Thing to their Purpose. I knew I had been here now almost eighteen Years, and never saw the least Foot-steps of Humane Creature there before; and I might be here eighteen more, as entirely conceal'd as I was now, if I did not discover my self to them, which I had no manner of Occasion to do, it being my only Business to keep my self entirely conceal'd where I was, unless I found a better sort of Creatures than *Canibals* to make my self known to.

Yet I entertain'd such an Abhorrence of the Savage Wretches, that I have been speaking of, and of the wretched inhuman Custom of their devouring and eating one another up, that I continu'd pensive, and sad, and kept close within my own Circle for almost two Years after this: When I say my own Circle, I mean by it, my three Plantations, *viz.* my Castle, my Country Seat, which I call'd my Bower, and my Enclosure in the Woods; nor did I look after this for any other Use than as an Enclosure for my Goats; for the Aversion which Nature gave me to these hellish Wretches, was such, that I was fearful of seeing them, as of seeing the Devil himself; nor did I so much as go to look after my Boat, in all this Time; but began rather to think of making me another; for I cou'd not think of ever making any more Attempts, to bring the other Boat round the Island to me, least I should meet with some of these Creatures at Sea, in which, if I had happen'd to have fallen into their Hands, I knew what would have been my Lot.

Time however, and the Satisfaction I had, that I was in no Danger of being discover'd by these People, began to wear off my Uneasiness about them; and I began to

live juſt in the same compos'd Manner as before; only
with this Difference, that I used more Caution, and kept
my Eyes more about me than I did before, leaſt I should
happen to be seen by any of them; and particularly, I was
more cautious of firing my Gun, leaſt any of them being
on the Island, should happen to hear of it: and it was
therefore a very good Pravidence to me, that I had furnish'd my self with a tame Breed of Goats, that I needed
not hunt any more about the Woods, or shoot at them;
and if I did catch any of them after this, it was by Traps,
and Snares, as I had done before; so that for two years
after this, I believe I never fir'd my Gun once of, though
I never went out without it; and which was more, as I had
sav'd three Piſtols out of the Ship, I always carry'd them
out with me, or at leaſt two of them, ſticking them in my
Goat-skin Belt; also I furbish'd up one of the great Cut-
lashes, that I had out of the Ship, and made me a Belt to
put it on also; so that I was now a moſt formidable Fellow
to look at, when I went abroad, if you add to the former
Description of my self, the Particular of two Piſtols, and
a great broad Sword hanging at my Side in a Belt, but
without a Scabbard.

Things going on thus, as I have said, for some Time; I
seem'd, excepting these Cautions, to be reduc'd to my
former calm, sedate Way of Living, all these Things
tended to shewing me more and more how far my Condition was from being miserable, compar'd to some others;
nay, to many other Particulars of Life, which it might
have pleased God to have made my Lot. It put me upon
reflecting, How little repining there would be among
Mankind, at any Condition of Life, if People would rather compare their Condition with those that are worse,
in order to be thankful, than be always comparing them

with those which are better, to assist their Murmurings and Complainings.

As in my present Condition there were not really many Things which I wanted; so indeed I thought that the Frights I had been in about these Savage Wretches, and the Concern I had been in for my own Preservation, had taken off the Edge of my Invention for my own Conveniences; and I had dropp'd a good Design, which I had once bent my Thoughts too much upon; and that was, to try if I could not make some of my Barley into Malt, and then try to brew my self some Beer: This was really a whimsical Thought, and I reprov'd my self often for the Simplicity of it; for I presently saw there would be the want of several Things necessary to the making my Beer, that it would be impossible for me to supply; as First, Casks to preserve it in, which was a Thing, that as I have observ'd already, I cou'd never compass; no, though I spent not many Days, but Weeks, nay, Months in attempting it, but to no purpose. In the next Place, I had no Hops to make it keep, no Yeast to make it work, no Copper or Kettle to make it boil; and yet all these Things, notwithstanding, I verily believe, had not these Things interven'd, I mean the Frights and Terrors I was in about the Savages, I had undertaken it, and perhaps brought it to pass too; for I seldom gave any Thing over without accomplishing it, when I once had it in my Head enough to begin it.

But my Invention now run quite another Way; for Night and Day, I could think of nothing but how I might destroy some of these Monsters in their cruel bloody Entertainment, and if possible, save the Victim they should bring hither to destroy. It would take up a larger Volume than this whole Work is intended to be, to set down all the Contrivances I hatch'd, or rather brooded upon in my Thought, for the destroying these Creatures, or at least frightening them, so as to prevent their coming hither any more; but all was abortive, nothing could be possible to take effect, unless I was to be there to do it my self; and what could one Man do among them, when perhaps there might be twenty or thirty of them together, with their Darts, or their Bows and Arrows, with which they could shoot as true to a Mark, as I could with my · Gun?

Sometimes I contriv'd to dig a Hole under the Place where they made their Fire, and put in five or six Pound of Gun-Powder, which when they kindled their Fire, would consequently take Fire, and blow up all that was near it: but as in the first place I should be very loth to wast so much Powder upon them, my Store being now within the Quantity of one Barrel; so neither could I be sure of its going off, at any certain Time; when it might surprise them, and at best, that it would do little more than just blow the Fire about their Ears and fright them, but not sufficient to make them forsake the Place; so I laid it aside, and then propos'd, that I would place my self in Ambush, in some convenient Place, with my three Guns, all double loaded; and in the middle of their bloody Ceremony, let fly at them, when I should be sure to kill or wound perhaps two or three at every shoot; and then falling in upon them with my three Pistols, and my Sword, I made no doubt, but that if there was twenty I should kill them all: This Fancy pleas'd my Thoughts for some Weeks, and I was so full of it, that I often dream'd of it; and sometimes that I was just going to let fly at them in my Sleep.

I went so far with it in my Imagination, that I employ'd my self several Days to find out proper Places to put my self in Ambuscade, as I said, to watch for them; and I went frequently to the Place it self, which was now grown more familiar to me; and especially while my Mind was thus fill'd with Thoughts of Revenge, and of a bloody putting twenty or thirty of them to the Sword, as I may call it; the Horror I had at the Place, and at the Signals of the barbarous Wretches devouring one another, abated my Malice.

Well, at length I found a Place in the Side of the Hill, where I was satisfy'd I might securely wait, till I saw any of their Boats coming, and might then, even before they would be ready to come on Shore, convey my self unseen into Thickets of Trees, in one of which there was a Hollow large enough to conceal me entirely; and where I might sit and observe all their bloody Doings, and take my full aim at their Heads, when they were so close together, as that it would be next to impossible that I should miss my Shoot, or that I could fail wounding three or four of them at the first Shoot.

In this Place then I resolv'd to fix my Design, and accordingly I prepar'd two Muskets, and my ordinary Fowling Piece. The two Muskets I loaded with a Brace of Slugs each, and four or five smaller Bullets, about the Size of Pistol Bullets; and the Fowling Piece I loaded with near a Handful of Swan-shot, of the largest Size; I also loaded my Pistols with about four Bullets each, and in this Posture, well provided with Ammunition for a second and third Charge, I prepar'd my self for my Expedition.

After I had thus laid the Scheme of my Design, and in my Imagination put it in Practice, I continually made my Tour every Morning up to the Top of the Hill, which

was from my Caſtle, as I call'd it, about three Miles, or
more, to see if I cou'd observe any Boats upon the Sea,
coming near the Island, or ſtanding over towards it; but
I began to tire of this hard Duty; after I had for two or
three Months conſtantly kept my Watch; but came always back without any Discovery, there having not in all
that Time been the leaſt Appearance, not only on, or
near the Shore; but not on the whole Ocean, so far as my
Eyes or Glasses could reach every Way.

As long as I kept up my daily Tour to the Hill, to look
out; so long also I kept up the Vigour of my Design, and
my Spirits seem'd to be all the while in a suitable Form,
for so outragious an Execution as the killing twenty or
thirty naked Savages, for an Offence which I had not at
all entred into a Discussion of in my Thoughts, any farther than my Passions were at firſt fir'd by the Horror I
conceiv'd at the unnatural Cuſtom of that People of the
Country, who it seems had been suffer'd by Providence
in his wise Disposition of the World, to have no other
Guide than that of their own abominable and vitiated
Passions; and consequently were left, and perhaps had
been so for some Ages, to aƈt such horrid Things, and receive such dreadful Cuſtoms, as nothing but Nature entirely abandon'd of Heaven, and aƈted by some hellish
Degeneracy, could have run them into: But now, when
as I have said, I began to be weary of the fruitless Excursion, which I had made so long, and so far, every Morning in vain, so my Opinion of the Aƈtion it self began to
alter, and I began with cooler and calmer Thoughts to
consider what it was I was going to engage in. What Authority, or Call I had, to pretend to be Judge and Executioner upon these Men as Criminals, whom Heaven had
thought fit for so many Ages to suffer unpunish'd, to go

on, and to be as it were, the Executioners of his Judgments one upon another. How far these People were Offenders against me, and what Right I had to engage in the Quarrel of that Blood, which they shed promiscuously one upon another. I debated this very often with my self thus; How do I know what God himself judges in this particular Case; it is certain these People either do not commit this as a Crime; it is not against their own Consciences reproving, or their Light reproaching them. They do not know it be an Offence, and then commit it in Defiance of Divine Justice, as we do in almost all the Sins we commit, They think it no more a Crime to kill a Captive taken in War, than we do to kill an Ox; nor to eat humane Flesh, than we do to eat Mutton.

When I had consider'd this a little, it follow'd necessarily, that I was certainly in the Wrong in it, that these People were not Murtherers, in the Sense that I had before condemn'd them, in my Thoughts; any more than those Christians were Murtherers, who often put to Death the Prisoners taken in Battle; or more frequently, upon many Occasions, put whole Troops of Men to the Sword, without giving Quarter, though they threw down their Arms and submitted.

In the next Place it occurr'd to me, that albeit the Usage they thus gave one another, was thus brutish and inhumane; yet it was really nothing to me: These People had done me no Injury. That if they attempted me, or I saw it necessary for my immediate Preservation to fall upon them, something might be said for it; but that as I was yet out of their Power, and they had really no Knowledge of me, and consequently no Design upon me; and therefore it could not be just for me to fall upon them. That this would justify the Conduct of the *Spaniards* in all their

Barbarities practis'd in *America*, where they destroy'd
Millions of these People, who however they were Idola-
ters and Barbarians, and had several bloody and barbarous Rites in their Customs, such as sacrificing human
Bodies to their Idols, were yet, as to the *Spaniards*, very
innocent People; and that the rooting them out of the
Country, is spoken of with the utmost Abhorrence and
Detestation, by even the *Spaniards* themselves, at this
Time; and by all other Christian Nations of *Europe*, as a
meer Butchery, a bloody and unnatural Piece of Cruelty,
unjustifiable either to God or Man; and such, as for which
the very Name of a *Spaniard* is reckon'd to be frightful
and terrible to all People of Humanity, or of Christian
Compassion: As if the Kingdom of *Spain* were particularly Eminent for the Product of a Race of Men, who
were without Principles of Tenderness, or the common
Bowels of Pity to the Miserable, which is reckon'd to be a
Mark of generous Temper in the Mind.

These Considerations really put me to a Pause, and to
a kind of a Full-stop; and I began by little and little to be
off of my Design, and to conclude, I had taken wrong
Measures in my Resolutions to attack the Savages; that
it was not my Business to meddle with them, unless they
first attack'd me, and this it was my Business if possible
to prevent; but that if I were discover'd, and attack'd,
then I knew my Duty.

On the other hand, I argu'd with my self, That this
really was the way not to deliver my self, but entirely to
ruin and destroy my self; for unless I was sure to kill every
one that not only should be on Shore at that Time, but
that should ever come on Shore afterwards, if but one of
them escap'd, to tell their Country People what had happen'd, they would come over again by Thousands to re-

venge the Death of their Fellows, and I should only bring upon my self a certain Deſtruction, which at present I had no manner of occasion for.

Upon the whole I concluded, That neither in Principle or in Policy, I ought one way or other to concern my self in this Affair. That my Business was by all possible Means to conceal my self from them, and not to leave the leaſt Signal to them to guess by, that there were any living Creatures upon the Island; I mean of humane Shape.

Religion joyn'd in with this Prudential, and I was convinc'd now many Ways, that I was perfectly out of my Duty, when I was laying all my bloody Schemes for the Deſtruction of innocent Creatures, I mean innocent as to me: As to the Crimes they were guilty of towards one another, I had nothing to do with them; they were National, and I ought to leave them to the Juſtice of God, who is the Governour of Nations, and knows how by National Punishments to make a juſt Retribution for National Offences; and to bring publick Judgments upon those who offend in a publick Manner, by such Ways as beſt pleases him.

This appear'd so clear to me now, that nothing was a greater Satisfaction to me, than that I had not been suffer'd to do a Thing which I now saw so much Reason to believe would have been no less a Sin, than that of wilful Murther, if I had committed it; and I gave moſt humble Thanks on my Knees to God, that had thus deliver'd me from Blood-Guiltiness; beseeching him to grant me the Protection of his Providence, that I might not fall into the Hands of the Barbarians; or that I might not lay my Hands upon them, unless I had a more clear Call from Heaven to do it, in Defence of my own Life.

In this Disposition I continu'd, for near a Year after

this; and so far was I from desiring an Occasion for falling upon these Wretches, that in all that Time, I never once went up the Hill to see whether there were any of them in Sight, or to know whether any of them had been on Shore there, or not, that I might not be tempted to renew any of my Contrivances against them, or be provok'd by any Advantage which might present it self, to fall upon them; only this I did, I went and remov'd my Boat, which I had on the other Side the Island, and carry'd it down to the *East* End of the whole Island, where I ran it into a little Cove which I found under some high Rocks, and where I knew, by Reason of the Currents, the Savages durst not, at least would not come with their Boats, upon any Account whatsoever.

With my Boat I carry'd away every Thing that I had left there belonging to her, though not necessary for the bare going thither, *viz.* A Mast and Sail which I had made for her, and a Thing like an Anchor, but indeed which could not be call'd either Anchor or Grapling; however, it was the best I could make of its kind: All these I remov'd, that there might not be the least Shadow of any Discovery, or any Appearance of any Boat, or of any human Habitation upon the Island.

Besides this, I kept my self, as I said, more retir'd than ever, and seldom went from my Cell, other than upon my constant Employment, *viz.* To milk my She-goats, and manage my little Flock, in the Wood; which as it was quite on the other Part of the Island, was quite out of Danger; for certain it is, that these Savage People who sometimes haunted this Island, never came with any Thoughts of finding any Thing here; and consequently never wandred off from the Coast; and I doubt not, but they might have been several Times on Shore, after my

Apprehensions of them had made me cautious as well as before; and indeed, I look'd back with some Horror upon the Thoughts of what my Condition would have been, if I had chop'd upon them, and been discover'd before that, when naked and unarm'd, except with one Gun, and that loaden often only with small Shot, I walk'd every where peeping, and peeping about the Island, to see what I could get; what a Surprise should I have been in, if when I discover'd the Print of a Man's Foot, I had instead of that, seen fifteen or twenty Savages, and found them pursuing me, and by the Swiftness of their Running, no Possibility of my escaping them.

The Thoughts of this sometimes sunk my very Soul within me, and distress'd my Mind so much, that I could not soon recover it, to think what I should have done, and how I not only should not have been able to resist them, but even should not have had Presence of Mind enough to do what I might have done; much less, what now after so much Consideration and Preparation I might be able to do: Indeed, after serious thinking of these Things, I should be very Melancholy; and sometimes it would last a great while; but I resolv'd it at last all into Thankfulness to that Providence, which had deliver'd me from so many unseen Dangers, and had kept me from those Mischiefs which I could no way have been the Agent in delivering my self from; because I had not the least Notion of any such Thing depending, or the least Supposition of it being possible.

This renew'd a Contemplation, which often had come to my Thoughts in former Time, when first I began to see the merciful Dispositions of Heaven, in the Dangers we run through in this Life. How wonderfully we are deliver'd, when we know nothing of it. How when we are in (a *Quandary*, as we call it) a Doubt or Hesitation, whether to go this Way, or that Way, a secret Hint shall direct us this Way, when we intended to go that Way; nay, when Sense, our own Inclination, and perhaps Business has call'd to go the other Way, yet a strange Impression upon the Mind, from we know not what Springs, and by we know not what Power, shall over-rule us to go this Way; and it shall afterwards appear, that had we gone thatWay which we should have gone, and even to our Imagination ought to have gone, we should have been ruin'd and lost: Upon these, and many like Reflections, I afterwards made it a certain Rule with me, That whenever I found those se-cret Hints, or pressings of my Mind, to doing, or not do-ing any Thing that presented; or to going this Way, or thatWay, I never fail'd to obey the secret Dictate; though I knew no other Reason for it, than that such a Pressure, or such a Hint hung upon my Mind: I could give many Examples of the Success of this Conduct in the Course of my Life; but more especially in the latter Part of my in-habiting this unhappy Island; besides many Occasions which it is very likely I might have taken Notice of, if I had seen with the same Eyes then, that I saw with now: But 'tis never too late to be wise; and I cannot but advise all considering Men, whose Lives are attended with such extraordinary Incidents as mine, or even though not so extraordinary, not to slight such secret Intimations of Providence, let them come from what invisible Intelli-gence they will, that I shall not discuss, and perhaps can-not account for; but certainly they are a Proof of the Con-verse of Spirits, and the secret Communication between those embody'd, and those unembody'd; and such a Proof as can never be withstood: Of which I shall have Occasion to give some very remarkable Instances, in the Remainder of my solitary Residence in this dismal Place.

I believe the Reader of this will not think ſtrange, if I confess that these Anxieties, these conſtant Dangers I liv'd in, and the Concern that was now upon me, put an End to all Invention, and to all the Contrivances that I had laid for my future Accommodations and Conveniencies. I had the Care of my Safety more now upon my Hands, than that of my Food. I car'd not to drive a Nail, or chop a Stick of Wood now, for fear the Noise I should make should be heard; much less would I fire a Gun, for the same Reason; and above all, I was intollerably uneasy at making any Fire, leaſt the Smoke which is visible at a great Diſtance in the Day should betray me; and for this Reason I remov'd that Part of my Business which requir'd Fire; such as burning of Pots, and Pipes, *etc.* into my new Apartment in the Woods, where after I had been some time, I found to my unspeakable Consolation, a meer natural Cave in the Earth, which went in a vaſt way, and where, I dare say, no Savage, had he been at the Mouth of it, would be so hardy as to venture in, nor indeed, would any Man else; but one who like me, wanted nothing so much as a safe Retreat.

The Mouth of this Hollow, was at the Bottom of a great Rock, where by meer accident, (I would say, if I did not see abundant Reason to ascribe all such Things now to Providence) I was cutting down some thick Branches of Trees, to make Charcoal; and before I go on, I muſt observe the Reason of my making this Charcoal; which was thus:

I was afraid of making a Smoke about my Habitation, as I said before; and yet I could not live there without baking my Bread, cooking my Meat, *&c.* so I contriv'd to burn some Wood here, as I had seen done in *England*, under Turf, till it became Chark, or dry Coal; and then putting the Fire out, I preserv'd the Coal to carry Home; and perform the other Services which Fire was wanting for at Home without Danger of Smoke.

But this is by the by: While I was cutting down some Wood here, I perceiv'd that behind a very thick Branch of low Brushwood, or Underwood, there was a kind of hollow Place; I was curious to look into it, and getting with Difficulty into the Mouth of it, I found it was pretty large; that is to say, sufficient for me to stand upright in it, and perhaps another with me; but I must confess to you, I made more hast out than I did in, when looking farther into the Place, and which was perfectly dark, I saw two broad shining Eyes of some Creature, whether Devil or Man I knew not, which twinkl'd like two Stars, the dim Light from the Cave's Mouth shining directly in and making the Reflection.

However, after some Pause, I recover'd my self, and began to call my self a thousand Fools, and tell my self, that he that was afraid to see the Devil, was not fit to live twenty Years in an Island all alone; and that I durst to believe there was nothing in this Cave that was more frightful than my self; upon this, plucking up my Courage, I took up a great Firebrand, and in I rush'd again, with the Stick flaming in my Hand; I had not gone three Steps in, but I was almost as much frighted as I was before; for I heard a very loud Sigh, like that of a Man in some Pain, and it was follow'd by a broken Noise, *as if* of Words half express'd, and then a deep Sigh again: I stepp'd back, and was indeed struck with such a Surprize, that it put me into a cold Sweat; and if I had had a Hat on my Head, I will not answer for it, that my Hair might not have lifted it off. But still plucking up my Spirits as well as I could, and encouraging my self a little with considering that the Power and Presence of God was every where, and was able to protect me; upon this I stepp'd forward again, and by the Light of the Firebrand, holding it up a little over my Head, I saw lying on the Ground a most monstrous frightful old He-goat, just making his Will, as we say, and gasping for Life, and dying indeed of meer old Age.

I stirr'd him a little to see if I could get him out, and he essay'd to get up, but was not able to raise himself; and I thought with my self, he might even lie there; for if he had frighted me so, he would certainly fright any of the Savages, if any of them should be so hardy as to come in there, while he had any Life in him.

I was now recover'd from my Surprize, and began to look round me, when I found the Cave was but very small, that is to say, it might be about twelve Foot over, but in no manner of Shape, either round or square, no Hands having ever been employ'd in making it, but those of meer Nature: I observ'd also, that there was a Place at the farther Side of it, that went in farther, but was so low, that it requir'd me to creep upon my Hands and Knees to go into it, and whither I went I knew not; so having no Candle, I gave it over for some Time; but resolv'd to come again the next Day, provided with Candles, and a Tinder-box, which I had made of the Lock of one of the Muskets, with some wild-fire in the Pan.

Accordingly the next Day, I came provided with six large Candles of my own making; for I made very good Candles now of Goat's Tallow; and going into this low Place, I was oblig'd to creep upon all Fours, *as I have said*, almost ten Yards; which by the way, I thought was a Venture bold enough, considering that I knew not how

far it might go, nor what was beyond it. When I was got
through the Strait, I found the Roof rose higher up, I believe near twenty Foot; but never was such a glorious
Sight seen in the Island, I dare say, as it was, to look round
the Sides and Roof of this Vault, or Cave; the Walls reflected 100 thousand Lights to me from my two Candles;
what it was in the Rock, whether Diamonds, or any other
precious Stones, or Gold, which I rather suppos'd it to be,
I knew not.

The Place I was in, was a most delightful Cavity, or
Grotto, of its kind, as could be expected, though perfectly dark; the Floor was dry and level, and had a sort of
small lose Gravel upon it, so that there was no nauseous
or venomous Creature to be seen, neither was there any
damp, or wet, on the Sides or Roof: The only Difficulty
in it was the Entrance, which however as it was a Place of
Security, and such a Retreat as I wanted, I thought that
was a Convenience; so that I was really rejoyc'd at the
Discovery, and resolv'd without any Delay, to bring some
of those Things which I was most anxious about, to this
Place; particularly, I resolv'd to bring hither my Magazine of Powder, and all my spare Arms, *viz.* Two Fowling-Pieces, for I had three in all; and three Muskets, for
of them I had eight in all; so I kept at my Castle only five,
which stood ready mounted like Pieces of Cannon, on my
out-most Fence; and were ready also to take out upon
any Expedition.

Upon this Occasion of removing my Ammunition, I
took occasion to open the Barrel of Powder which I took
up out of the Sea, and which had been wet; and I found
that the Water had penetrated about three or four Inches
into the Powder, on every Side, which caking and growing hard, had preserv'd the inside like a Kernel in a Shell;

so that I had near sixty Pound of very good Powder in the Center of the Cask, and this was an agreeable Discovery to me at that Time; so I carry'd all away thither, never keeping above two or three Pound of Powder with me in my Castle, for fear of a Surprize of any kind : I also carried thither all the Lead I had left for Bullets.

I fancy'd my self now like one of the ancient Giants, which are said to live in Caves, and Holes, in the Rocks, where none could come at them; for I perswaded my self while I was here, if five hundred Savages were to hunt me, they could never find me out; or if they did, they would not venture to attack me here.

The old Goat who I found expiring, dy'd in the Mouth of the Cave, the next Day after I made this Discovery; and I found it much easier to dig a great Hole there, and throw him in, and cover him with Earth, than to drag him out; so I interr'd him there, to prevent the Offence to my Nose.

I was now in my twenty third Year of Residence in this Island, and was so naturaliz'd to the Place, and to the Manner of Living, that could I have but enjoy'd the Certainty that no Savages would come to the Place to disturb me, I could have been content to have capitulated for spending the rest of my Time there, even to the last Moment, till I had laid me down and dy'd, like the old Goat in the Cave. I had also arriv'd to some little Diversions and Amusements, which made the Time pass more pleasantly with me a great deal, than it did before; as First, I had taught my Poll, as I noted before, to speak; and he did it so familiarly, and talk'd so articulately and plain, that it was very pleasant to me; and he liv'd with me no less than six and twenty Years : How long he might live afterwards, I know not; though I know they have a Notion in the *Brasils*, that they live a hundred Years; perhaps poor Poll may be alive there ſtill, calling after *Poor Robin Crusoe* to this Day. I wish no *English* Man the ill Luck to come there and hear him; but if he did, he would certainly believe it was the Devil. My Dog was a very pleasant and loving Companion to me, for no less than sixteen Years of my Time, and then dy'd, of meer old Age; as for my Cats, they multiply'd as I have observ'd to that Degree, that I was oblig'd to shoot several of them at firſt, to keep them from devouring me, and all I had; but at length, when the two old Ones I had brought with me were gone, and after some time continually driving them from me, and letting them have no Provision with me, they all ran wild into the Woods, except two or three Favourites, which I kept tame; and whose Young when they had any, I always drown'd; and these were part of my Family: Besides these, I always kept two or three houshold Kids about me, who I taught to feed out of my Hand; and I had two more Parrots which talk'd pretty well, and would all call *Robin Crusoe*; but none like my firſt; nor indeed did I take the Pains with any of them that I had done with him. I had also several tame Sea-Fowls, whose Names I know not, who I caught upon the Shore, and cut their Wings; and the little Stakes which I had planted before my Caſtle Wall being now grown up to a good thick Grove, these Fowls all liv'd among these low Trees, and bred there, which was very agreeable to me; so that as I said above, I began to be very well contented with the Life I led, if it might but have been secur'd from the dread of the Savages.

But it was otherwise direĉted; and it may not be amiss for all People who shall meet with my Story, to make this juſt Observation from it, *viz.* How frequently in the

Course of our Lives, the Evil which in it self we seek most to shun, and which when we are fallen into it, is the most dreadful to us, is oftentimes the very Means or Door of our Deliverance, by which alone we can be rais'd again from the Affliction we are fallen into. I cou'd give many Examples of this in the Course of my unaccountable Life; but in nothing was it more particularly remarkable, than in the Circumstances of my last Years of solitary Residence in this Island.

It was now the Month of *December*, as I said above, in my twenty third Year; and this being the *Southern* Solstice, for Winter I cannot call it, was the Particular Time of my Harvest, and requir'd my being pretty much abroad in the Fields, when going out pretty early in the Morning, even before it was thorow Day-light, I was surpriz'd with seeing a Light of some Fire upon the Shore, at a Distance from me, of about two Mile towards the End of the Island, where I had observ'd some Savages had been as before; but not on the other Side; but to my great Affliction, it was on my Side of the Island.

I was indeed terribly surpriz'd at the Sight, and stepp'd short within my Grove, not daring to go out, least I might be surpriz'd; and yet I had no more Peace within, from the Apprehensions I had, that if these Savages in rambling over the Island, should find my Corn standing, or cut, or any of my Works and Improvements, they would immediately conclude, that there were People in the Place, and would then never give over till they had found me out: In this Extremity I went back directly to my Castle, pull'd up the Ladder after me, and made all Things without look as wild and natural as I could.

Then I prepar'd my self within, putting my self in a Posture of Defence; I loaded all my Cannon, as I call'd them; that is to say, my Muskets, which were mounted upon my new Fortification, and all my Pistols, and resolv'd to defend my self to the last Gasp, not forgetting seriously to commend my self to the Divine Protection, and earnestly to pray to God to deliver me out of the Hands of the Barbarians; and in this Posture I continu'd about two Hours; but began to be mighty impatient for Intelligence abroad, for I had no Spies to send out.

After sitting a while longer, and musing what I should do in this Case, I was not able to bear sitting in Ignorance any longer; so setting up my Ladder to the Side of the Hill, where there was a flat Place, as I observ'd before, and then pulling the Ladder up after me, I set it up again, and mounted to the Top of the Hill; and pulling out my Perspective Glass, which I had taken on Purpose, I laid me down flat on my Belly, on the Ground, and began to look for the Place; I presently found there was no less than nine naked Savages, sitting round a small Fire, they had made, not to warm them; for they had no need of that, the Weather being extreme hot; but as I suppos'd, to dress some of their barbarous Diet, of humane Flesh, which they had brought with them, whether alive or dead I could not know.

They had two *Canoes* with them, which they had haled up upon the Shore; and as it was then Tide of Ebb, they seem'd to me to wait for the Return of the Flood, to go away again; it is not easy to imagine what Confusion this Sight put me into, especially seeing them come on my Side the Island, and so near me too; but when I observ'd their coming must always be with the Current of the Ebb, I began afterwards to be more sedate in my Mind, being satisfy'd that I might go abroad with Safety all the Time of the Tide of Flood, if they were not on Shore before:

And having made this Observation, I went abroad about my Harvest Work with the more Composure.

As I expected, so it proved; for as soon as the Tide made to the *Westward*, I saw them all take Boat, and row (or paddle as we call it) all away: I should have observ'd, that for an Hour and more before they went off, they went to dancing, and I could easily discern their Postures, and Gestures, by my Glasses: I could not perceive by my nicest Observation, but that they were stark naked, and had not the least covering upon them; but whether they were Men or Women, that I could not distinguish.

As soon as I saw them shipp'd, and gone, I took two Guns upon my Shoulders, and two Pistols at my Girdle, and my great Sword by my Side, without a Scabbard, and with all the Speed I was able to make, I went away to the Hill, where I had discover'd the first Appearance of all; and as soon as I gat thither, which was not less than two Hours (for I could not go apace, being so loaden with Arms as I was) I perceiv'd there had been three *Canoes* more of Savages on that Place; and looking out farther, I saw they were all at Sea together, making over for the Main.

This was a dreadful Sight to me, especially when going down to the Shore, I could see the marks of Horror, which the dismal Work they had been about had left behind it, *viz.* The Blood, the Bones, and part of the Flesh of humane Bodies, eaten and devour'd by those Wretches, with Merriment and Sport; I was so fill'd with Indignation at the Sight, that I began now to premeditate the Destruction of the next that I saw there, let them be who, or how many soever.

It seem'd evident to me, that the Visits which they thus make to this Island, are not very frequent; for it was above fifteen Months before any more of them came on Shore there again; that is to say, I neither saw them, or any Footsteps, or Signals of them, in all that Time; for as to the rainy Seasons, then they are sure not to come abroad, at least not so far; yet all this while I liv'd uncomfortably, by reason of the constant Apprehensions I was in of their coming upon me by Surprize; from whence I observe, that the Expectation of Evil is more bitter than the Suffering, especially, if there is no room to shake off that Expectation, or those Apprehensions.

During all this Time, I was in the murthering Humour; and took up most of my Hours, which should have been better employ'd, in contriving how to circumvent, and fall upon them, the very next Time I should see them; especially if they should be divided, as they were the last Time, into two Parties; nor did I consider at all, that if I kill'd one Party, suppose Ten, or a Dozen, I was still the next Day, or Week, or Month, to kill another, and so another, even *ad infinitum,* till I should be at length no less a Murtherer than they were in being Man-eaters; and perhaps much more so.

I spent my Days now in great Perplexity, and Anxiety of Mind, expecting that I should one Day or other fall into the Hands of these merciless Creatures; and if I did at any Time venture abroad, it was not without looking round me with the greatest Care and Caution imaginable; and now I found to my great Comfort, how happy it was that I provided for a tame Flock or Herd of Goats; for I durst not upon any account fire my Gun, especially near that Side of the Island where they usually came, least I should alarm the Savages; and if they had fled from me now, I was sure to have them come back again, with perhaps two or three hundred *Canoes* with them, in a few Days, and then I knew what to expect.

However, I wore out a Year and three Months more, before I ever saw any more of the Savages, and then I found them again, as I shall soon observe. It is true, they might have been there once, or twice; but either they made no ſtay, or at leaſt I did not hear them; but in the Month of *May*, as near as I could calculate, and in my four and twentieth Year, I had a very ſtrange Encounter with them, of which in its Place.

The Perturbation of my Mind, during this fifteen or sixteen Months Interval, was very great; I slept unquiet, dream'd always frightful Dreams, and often ſtarted out of my Sleep in the Night: In the Day great Troubles over-whelm'd my Mind, and in the Night I dream'd often of killing the Savages, and of the Reasons why I might juſti-fy the doing of it; but to wave all this for a while; it was in the middle of *May*, on the sixteenth Day I think, as well as my poor wooden Calendar would reckon; for I markt all upon the Poſt ſtill; I say, it was the sixteenth of *May*, that it blew a very great Storm of Wind, all Day, with a great deal of Lightning, and Thunder, and a very foul Night it was after it; I know not what was the particular Occasion of it; but as I was reading in the Bible, and tak-en up with very serious Thoughts about my present Con-dition, I was surpriz'd with a Noise of a Gun as I thought fir'd at Sea.

This was to be sure a Surprize of a quite different Na-ture from any I had met with before; for the Notions this put into my Thoughts, were quite of another kind. I ſtarted up in the greateſt haſt imaginable, and in a trice clapt my Ladder to the middle Place of the Rock, and pull'd it after me, and mounting it the second Time, got to the Top of the Hill, the very Moment, that a Flash of Fire bid me liſten for a second Gun, which accordingly,

in about half a Minute I heard; and by the sound, knew
that it was from that Part of the Sea where I was driven
down the Current in my Boat.

I immediately consider'd that this muſt be some Ship
in Diſtress, and that they had some Comrade, or some
other Ship in Company, and fir'd these Guns for Signals
of Diſtress, and to obtain Help: I had this Presence of
Mind at that Minute, as to think that though I could not
help them, it may be they might help me; so I brought together all the dry Wood I could get at hand, and making
a good handsome Pile, I set it on Fire upon the Hill; the
Wood was dry, and blaz'd freely; and though the Wind
blew very hard, yet it burnt fairly out; that I was certain,
if there was any such Thing as a Ship, they muſt needs
see it, and no doubt they did; for as soon as ever my Fire
blaz'd up, I heard another Gun, and after that several
others, all from the same Quarter; I ply'd my Fire all
Night long, till Day broke; and when it was broad Day,
and the Air clear'd up, I saw something at a great Distance at Sea, full *Eaſt* of the Island, whether a Sail, or a
Hull, I could not diſtinguish, no not with my Glasses, the
Diſtance was so great, and the Weather ſtill something
haizy also; at leaſt it was so out at Sea.

I look'd frequently at it all that Day, and soon perceiv'd that it did not move; so I presently concluded, that
it was a Ship at an Anchor, and being eager, you may be
sure, to be satisfy'd, I took my Gun in my Hand, and run
toward the *South* Side of the Island, to the Rocks where I
had formerly been carry'd away with the Current, and
getting up there, the Weather by this Time being perfeᶜtly clear, I could plainly see to my great Sorrow, the
Wreck of a Ship caſt away in the Night, upon those con-
cealed Rocks which I found, when I was out in my Boat;

and which Rocks, as they check'd the Violence of the Stream, and made a kind of Counter-ſtream, or Eddy, were the Occaſion of my recovering from the moſt deſperate hopeleſs Condition that ever I had been in, in all my Life.

Thus what is one Man's Safety, is another Man's Deſtruction; for it seems these Men, whoever they were, being out of their Knowledge, and the Rocks being wholly under Water, had been driven upon them in the Night, the Wind blowing hard at *E*. and *E.N.E*: Had they seen the Island, as I muſt necessarily suppose they did not, they muſt, as I thought have endeavour'd to have sav'd themselves on Shore by the Help of their Boat; but their firing of Guns for Help, especially when they saw, as I imagin'd, my Fire, fill'd me with many Thoughts: Firſt, I imagin'd that upon seeing my Light, they might have put themselves into their Boat, and have endeavour'd to make the Shore; but that the Sea going very high, they might have been caſt away; other Times I imagin'd, that they might have loſt their Boat before, as might be the Case many Ways; as particularly by the Breaking of the Sea upon their Ship, which many Times obliges Men to ſtave, or take in Pieces their Boat; and sometimes to throw it over-board with their own Hands: Other Times I imagin'd, they had some other Ship, or Ships in Company, who upon the Signals of Diſtress they had made, had taken them up, and carry'd them off: Other whiles I fancy'd, they were all gone off to Sea in their Boat, and being hurry'd away by the Current that I had been formerly in, were carry'd out into the great Ocean, where there was nothing but Misery and Perishing; and that perhaps they might by this Time think of ſtarving, and of being in a Condition to eat one another.

As all these were but Conjectures at best; so in the Condition I was in, I could do no more than look on upon the Misery of the poor Men, and pity them, which had still this good Effect on my Side that it gave me more and more Cause to give Thanks to God who had so happily and comfortably provided for me in my desolate Condition; and that of two Ships Companies who were now cast away upon this part of the World, not one Life should be spar'd but mine: I learn'd here again to observe, that it is very rare that the Providence of God casts us into any Condition of Life so low, or any Misery so great, but we may see something or other to be thankful for; and may see others in worse Circumstances than our own.

Such certainly was the Case of these Men, of whom I could not so much as see room to suppose any of them were sav'd; nothing could make it rational, so much as to wish, or expect that they did not all perish there; except the Possibility only of their being taken up by another Ship in Company, and this was but meer Possibility indeed; for I saw not the least Signal or Appearance of any such Thing.

I cannot explain by any possible Energy of Words what a strange longing or hankering of Desires I felt in my Soul upon this Sight; breaking out sometimes thus; O that there had been but one or two; nay, or but one Soul sav'd out of this Ship, to have escap'd to me, that I might but have had one Companion, one Fellow-Creature to have spoken to me, and to have convers'd with! In all the Time of my solitary Life, I never felt so earnest, so strong a Desire after the Society of my Fellow-Creatures, or so deep a Regret at the want of it.

There are some secret moving Springs in the Affections, which when they are set a going by some Object in view; or be it some Object, though not in view, yet rendred present to the Mind by the Power of Imagination, that Motion carries out the Soul by its Impetuosity to such violent eager embracings of the Object, that the Absence of it is insupportable.

Such were these earnest Wishings, That but one Man had been sav'd! *O that it had been but One!* I believe I repeated the Words, *O that it had been but One!* a thousand Times; and the Desires were so mov'd by it, that when I spoke the Words, my Hands would clinch together, and my Fingers press the Palms of my Hands, that if I had had any soft Thing in my Hand, it would have crusht it involuntarily; and my Teeth in my Head wou'd strike together, and set against one another so strong, that for some time I cou'd not part them again.

Let the Naturalists explain these Things, and the Reason and Manner of them; all I can say to them, is, to describe the Fact, which was even surprising to me when I found it; though I knew not from what it should proceed; it was doubtless the effect of ardent Wishes, and of strong Ideas form'd in my Mind, realizing the Comfort, which the Conversation of one of my Fellow-Christians would have been to me.

But it was not to be; either their Fate or mine, or both, forbid it; for till the last Year of my being on this Island, I never knew whether any were saved out of that Ship or no; and had only the Affliction some Days after, to see the Corps of a drownded Boy come on Shore, at the End of the Island which was next the Shipwreck: He had on no Cloaths, but a Seaman's Wastcoat, a pair of open knee'd Linnen Drawers, and a blew Linnen Shirt; but nothing to direct me so much as to guess what Nation he was of: He had nothing in his Pocket, but two Pieces of Eight, and a Tobacco- Pipe; the laſt was to me of ten times more value than the firſt.

It was now calm, and I had a great mind to venture out in my Boat, to this Wreck; not doubting but I might find something on board, that might be useful to me; but that did not altogether press me so much, as the Possibility that there might be yet some living Creature on board, whose Life I might not only save, but might by saving that Life, comfort my own to the laſt Degree; and this Thought clung so to my Heart, that I could not be quiet, Night or Day, but I muſt venture out in my Boat on board this Wreck; and committing the reſt to God's Providence, I thought the Impression was so ſtrong upon my Mind, that it could not be resiſted, that it muſt come from some invisible Direction, and that I should be wanting to my self if I did not go.

Under the Power of this Impression, I haſten'd back to my Caſtle, prepar'd every Thing for my Voyage, took a Quantity of Bread, a great Pot for fresh Water, a Compass to ſteer by, a Bottle of Rum; for I had ſtill a great deal of that left; a Basket full of Raisins: And thus loading my self with every Thing necessary; I went down to my Boat, got the Water out of her, and got her afloat, loaded all my Cargo in her, and then went Home again for more; my second Cargo was a great Bag full of Rice, the Umbrella to set up over my Head for Shade; another large Pot full of fresh Water, and about two Dozen of my small Loaves, or Barley Cakes, more than before, with a Bottle of Goat's-Milk, and a Cheese; all which, with great Labour and Sweat, I brought to my Boat; and praying to God to direct my Voyage, I put out, and Rowing or Padling the Canoe along the Shore, I came at laſt to the utmoſt Point of the Island on that Side, (*viz.*) *N.E.* And now I was to launch out into the Ocean, and either to venture, or not to venture. I look'd on the rapid Currents which ran conſtantly on both Sides of the Island, at a Diſtance, and which were very terrible to me, from the Remembrance of the Hazard I had been in before, and my Heart began to fail me; for I foresaw that if I was driven into either of those Currents, I should be carry'd a vaſt Way out to Sea, and perhaps out of my Reach, or Sight of the Island again; and that then, as my Boat was but small, if any little Gale of Wind should rise, I should be inevitably loſt.

These Thoughts so oppress'd my Mind, that I began to give over my Enterprize, and having haled my Boat into a little Creek on the Shore, I ſtept out, and sat me down upon a little rising bit of Ground, very pensive and anxious, between Fear and Desire about my Voyage; when as I was musing, I could perceive that the Tide was turn'd, and the Flood come on, upon which my going was for so many Hours impracticable; upon this presently it occurr'd to me, that I should go up to the higheſt Piece of Ground I could find, and observe, if I could, how the Sets of the Tide, or Currents lay, when the Flood came in, that I might judge whether if I was driven one way out, I might not expect to be driven another way home, with the same Rapidness of the Currents: This Thought was no sooner in my Head, but I caſt my Eye upon a little Hill, which sufficiently over-look'd the Sea both ways, and from whence I had a clear view of the Currents, or Sets of the Tide, and which way I was to guide my self in my Return; here I found, that as the Current of the Ebb set out close by the South Point of the Island; so the Current of the Flood set in close by the

Shore of the North Side, and that I had nothing to do but to keep to the North of the Island in my Return, and I should do well enough.

Encourag'd with this Observation, I resolv'd the Next Morning to set out with the firſt of the Tide; and reposing my self for the Night in the Canoe, under the great Watch-coat, I mention'd, I launched out: I made firſt a little out to Sea full North, till I began to feel the Benefit of the Current, which set Eaſtward, and which carry'd me at a great rate, and yet did not so hurry me as the Southern Side Current had done before, and so as to take from me all Government of the Boat; but having a ſtrong Steerage with my Paddle, I went at a great rate, direſtly for the Wreck, and in less than two Hours I came up to it.

It was a dismal Sight to look at: The Ship, which by its building was *Spanish*, ſtuck faſt, jaum'd in between two Rocks; all the Stern and Quarter of her was beaten to Pieces with the Sea; and as her Forecaſtle, which ſtuck in the Rocks, had run on with great Violence, her Mainmaſt and Foremaſt were brought by the Board; that is to say, broken short off; but her Boltsprit was sound and the Head and Bow appear'd firm; when I came close to her, a Dog appear'd upon her, who seeing me coming, yelp'd, and cry'd; and as soon as I call'd him, jump'd into the Sea, to come to me, and I took him into the Boat; but found him almoſt dead for Hunger and Thirſt: I gave him a Cake of my Bread, and he eat it like a ravenous Wolf, that had been ſtarving a Fortnight in the Snow: I then gave the poor Creature some fresh Water, with which, if I would have let him he would have burſt himself.

After this I went on board; but the firſt Sight I met with, was two Men drown'd, in the Cook-room, or Forecastle of the Ship, with their Arms fast about one another: I concluded, as is indeed probable, that when the Ship struck, it being in a Storm, the Sea broke so high, and so continually over her, that the Men were not able to bear it, and were strangled with the constant rushing in of the Water, as much as if they had been under Water. Besides the Dog, there was nothing left in the Ship that had life; nor any Goods that I could see, but what were spoil'd by the Water. There were some Casks of Liquor, whether Wine or Brandy, I knew not, which lay lower in the Hold; and which, the Water being ebb'd out, I could see; but they were too big to meddle with: I saw several Chests, which I believ'd belong'd to some of the Seamen; and I got two of them into the Boat, without examining what was in them.

Had the Stern of the Ship been fix'd, and the Forepart broken off, I am perswaded I might have made a good Voyage; for by what I found in these two Chests, I had room to suppose, the Ship had a great deal of Wealth on board; and if I may guess by the course she steer'd, she must have been bound from the *Buenos Ayres*, or the *Rio de la Plata*, in the South Part of *America*, beyond the *Brasils*, to the *Havana*, in the Gulph of *Mexico*, and so perhaps to *Spain*: She had no doubt a great Treasure in her; but of no Use at that Time to any Body; and what became of the rest of her People, I then knew not.

I found besides these Chests, a little Cask full of Liquor, of about twenty Gallons, which I got into my Boat, with much Difficulty; there were several Muskets in a Cabin, and a great Powder-horn, with about 4 Pounds of Powder in it; as for the Muskets I had no occasion for them; so I left them, but took the Powder-horn: I took a Fire Shovel and Tongs, which I wanted extremely; as al-

so two little Brass Kettles, a Copper Pot to make Cho-
colate, and a Gridiron; and with this Cargo, and the Dog,
I came away, the Tide beginning to make home again;
and the same Evening, about an Hour within Night, I
reach'd the Island again, weary and fatigu'd to the laſt
Degree.

I repos'd that Night in the Boat, and in the Morning I
resolved to harbour what I had gotten in my new Cave,
not to carry it home to my Caſtle. After refreshing my
self, I got all my Cargo on Shore, and began to examine
the Particulars: The Cask of Liquor I found to be a kind
of Rum, but not such as we had at the *Brasils*; and in a
Word, not at all good; but when I came to open the
Cheſts, I found several Things, of great Use to me: For
Example, I found in one, a fine Case of Bottles, of an
extraordinary kind, and fill'd with Cordial Waters, fine,
and very good; the Bottles held about three Pints each,
and were tipp'd with Silver: I found two Pots of very
good Succades, or Sweetmeats, so faſtned also on top,
that the Salt Water had not hurt them; and two more of
the same, which the Water had spoil'd: I found some
very good Shirts, which were very welcome to me; and
about a dozen and half of Linnen white Handkerchiefs,
and colour'd Neckcloths; the former were also very welcome, being exceeding refreshing to wipe my Face in a
hot Day; besides this, when I came to the Till in the
Cheſt, I found there three great Bags of Pieces of Eight,
which held about eleven hundred Pieces in all; and in
one of them, wrapt up in a Paper, six Doubloons of Gold,
and some small Bars or Wedges of Gold; I suppose they
might all weigh near a Pound.

The other Cheſt I found had some Cloaths in it, but of
little Value; but by the Circumſtances it muſt have be-

long'd to the Gunner's Mate; though there was no Powder in it; but about two Pound of fine glaz'd Powder, in
three small Flasks, kept, I suppose, for charging their
Fowling-Pieces on occasion: Upon the whole, I got very
little by this Voyage, that was of any use to me; for as to
the Money, I had no manner of occasion for it: 'Twas to
me as the Dirt under my Feet; and I would have given it
all for three or four pair of *English* Shoes and Stockings;
which were Things I greatly wanted, but had not had on
my Feet now for many Years: I had indeed gotten two
pair of Shoes now, which I took off of the Feet of the two
drown'd Men, who I saw in the Wreck; and I found two
pair more in one of the Chests, which were very welcome
to me; but they were not like our *English* Shoes, either for
Ease, or Service; being rather what we call Pumps, than
Shoes: I found in this Seaman's Chest, about fifty Pieces
of Eight in Ryals, but no Gold; I suppose this belong'd
to a poorer Man than the other, which seem'd to belong
to some Officer.

Well, however, I lugg'd this Money home to my Cave,
and laid it up, as I had done that before which I brought
from our own Ship; but it was great Pity as I said, that
the other Part of this Ship had not come to my Share; for
I am satisfy'd I might have loaded my *Canoe* several
Times over with Money, which if I had ever escap'd to
England, would have lain here safe enough, till I might
have come again and fetch'd it.

Having now brought all my Things on Shore, and secur'd them, I went back to my Boat, and row'd, or pad-
dled her along the Shore, to her old Harbour, where I
laid her up, and made the best of my way to my old Habitation, where I found everything safe and quiet; so I began to repose my self, live after my old Fashion, and take

care of my Family Affairs; and for a while, I liv'd easy enough; only that I was more vigilant than I us'd to be, look'd out oftner, and did not go abroad so much; and if at any time I did ſtir with any Freedom, it was always to the *Eaſt* Part of the Island, where I was pretty well satis-fy'd the Savages never came, and where I could go with-out so many Precautions, and such a Load of Arms and Ammunition, as I always carry'd with me, if I went the other way.

I liv'd in this Condition near two Years more; but my unlucky Head, that was always to let me know it was born to make my Body miserable, was all this two Years fill'd with Projeċts and Designs, how, if it were possible, I might get away from this Island; for sometimes I was for making another Voyage to the Wreck, though my Rea-son told me that there was nothing left there, worth the Hazard of my Voyage; Sometimes for a Ramble one way, sometimes another; and I believe verily, if I had had the Boat that I went from *Sallee* in, I should have ventur'd to Sea, bound any where, I knew not whither.

I have been in all my Circumſtances a *Memento* to those who are touched with the general Plague of Mankind, whence, for ought I know, one half of their Miseries flow; I mean, that of not being satisfy'd with the Station wherein God and Nature has plac'd them; for not to look back upon my primitive Condition, and the excellent Ad-vice of my Father, the Opposition to which, was, *as I may call it,* my O R I G I N A L S I N ; my subsequent Miſtakes of the same Kind had been the Means of my coming into this miserable Condition; for had that Providence, which so happily had seated me at the *Brasils,* as a Planter, bless'd me with confin'd Desires, and I could have been contented to have gone on gradually, I might have been by this Time; *I mean, in the Time of my being in this Island,* one of the moſt considerable Planters in the *Brasils,* nay, I am perswaded, that by the Improvements I had made, in that little Time I liv'd there, and the Encrease I should probably have made, if I had ſtay'd, I might have been worth an hundred thousand *Moydors*; and what Business had I to leave a settled Fortune, a well ſtock'd Plantation, improving and encreasing, to turn *Supra-Cargo* to *Guinea,* to fetch Negroes; when Patience and Time would have so encreas'd our Stock at Home, that we could have bought them at our own Door, from those whose Business it was to fetch them; and though it had coſt us something more, yet the Difference of that Price was by no Means worth saving, at so great a Hazard.

But as this is ordinarily the Fate of young Heads, so Refleſtion upon the Folly of it, is as ordinarily the Exercise of more Years, or of the dear bought Experience of Time; and so it was with me now; and yet so deep had the Miſtake taken root in my Temper, that I could not satisfy my self in my Station, but was continually poring upon the Means, and Possibility of my Escape from this Place; and that I may with the greater Pleasure to the Reader, bring on the remaining Part of my Story, it may not be improper, to give some Account of my firſt Conceptions on the Subjeſt of this foolish Scheme for my Escape; and how, and upon what Foundation I aſted.

I am now to be suppos'd retir'd into my Caſtle, after my late Voyage to the Wreck, my Frigate laid up, and secur'd under Water, as usual, and my Condition reſtor'd to what it was before: I had more Wealth indeed than I had before, but was not at all the richer; for I had no more use for it, than the *Indians* of *Peru* had, before the *Spaniards* came there.

It was one of the Nights in the rainy Season in *March*, the four and twentieth Year of my first setting Foot in this Island of Solitariness; I was lying in my bed, or Hammock, awake, very well in Health, had no Pain, no Distemper, no Uneasiness of Body; no, nor any Uneasiness of Mind, more than ordinary; but could by no means close my Eyes; that is, so as to sleep; no, not a Wink all Night long, otherwise than as follows:

It is as impossible, as needless, to set down the innumerable Crowd of Thoughts that whirl'd through that great thorow-fare of the Brain, the Memory, in this Night's Time: I run over the whole History of my Life in Miniature, or by Abridgement, *as I may call it*, to my coming to this Island, and also of the Part of my Life, since I came to this Island. In my Reflections upon the State of my Case, since I came on Shore on this Island, I was comparing the happy Posture of my Affairs, in the first Years of my Habitation here, compar'd to the Life of Anxiety, Fear and Care, which I had liv'd ever since I had seen the Print of a Foot in the Sand; not that I did not believe the Savages had frequented the Island even all the while, and might have been several Hundreds of them at Times on Shore there; but I had never known it, and was incapable of any Apprehensions about it; my Satisfaction was perfect, though my Danger was the same; and I was as happy in not knowing my Danger, as if I had never really been expos'd to it: This furnish'd my Thoughts with many very profitable Reflections, and particularly this one, How infinitely Good that Providence is, which has provided in its Government of Mankind, such narrow bounds to his Sight and Knowledge of Things, and though he walks in the midst of so many thousand Dangers, the Sight of which, if discover'd to him, would distract his Mind, and sink his Spirits; he is kept serene, and calm, by having the Events of Things hid from his Eyes, and knowing nothing of the Dangers which surround him.

After these Thoughts had for some Time entertain'd me, I came to reflect seriously upon the real Danger I had been in, for so many Years, in this very Island; and how I had walk'd about in the greatest Security, and with all possible Tranquillity; even when perhaps nothing but a Brow of a Hill, a great Tree, or the casual Approach of Night, had been between me and the worst kind of Destruction, *viz.* That of falling into the Hands of Cannibals, and Savages, who would have seiz'd on me with the same View, as I did of a Goat, or a Turtle; and have thought it no more a Crime to kill and devour me, than I did of a Pidgeon, or a Curlieu: I would unjustly slander my self, if I should say I was not sincerely thankful to my great Preserver, to whose singular Protection I acknowledg'd, with great Humility, that all these unknown Deliverances were due; and without which, I must inevitably have fallen into their merciless Hands.

When these Thoughts were over, my Head was for some time taken up in considering the Nature of these wretched Creatures; I mean, the Savages; and how it came to pass in the World, that the wise Governour of all Things should give up any of his Creatures to such Inhumanity; nay, to something so much below, even Brutality itself, as to devour its own Kind; but as this ended in some (at that Time fruitless) Speculations, it occurr'd to me to enquire, what Part of the World these Wretches liv'd in; how far off the Coast was from whence they came; what they ventur'd over so far from home for; what kind of Boats they had; and why I might not order my self, and my Business so, that I might be as able to go over thither, as they were to come to me.

I never so much as troubl'd my self, to consider what I should do with my self, when I came thither; what would become of me, if I fell into the Hands of the Savages; or how I should escape from them, if they attempted me; no, nor so much as how it was possible for me to reach the Coast, and not to be attempted by some or other of them, without any Possibliity of delivering my self; and if I should not fall into their Hands, what I should do for Provision, or whither I should bend my Course; none of these Thoughts, I say, so much as came in my way; but my mind was wholly bent upon the Notion of my passing over in my Boat, to the Main Land: I look'd back upon my present Condition, as the most miserable that could possibly be, that I was not able to throw my self into any thing but Death, that could be call'd worse; that if I reached the Shore of the Main, I might perhaps meet with Relief, or I might coast along, as I did on the Shore of *Africk*, till I came to some inhabited Country, and where I might find some Relief; and after all perhaps, I might fall in with some Christian Ship, that might take me in; and if the worse came to the worst, I could but die, which would put an end to all these Miseries at once. Pray note, all this was the fruit of a disturb'd Mind, an impatient Temper, made as it were desperate by the long Continuance of my Troubles and the Disappointments I had met in the Wreck, I had been on board of; and where I had been so near the obtaining what I so earnestly long'd for, *viz.* Some-Body to speak to, and to learn some Knowledge from of the Place where I was, and of the probable Means of my Deliverance; I say, I was agitated wholly by these Thoughts: All my Calm of Mind in my Resigna-

tion to Providence, and waiting the Issue of the Dispositions of Heaven, seem'd to be suspended; and I had, as it
were, no Power to turn my Thoughts to any thing, but to
the Project of a Voyage to the Main, which came upon
me with such Force, and such an Impetuosity of Desire,
that it was not to be resisted.

When this had agitated my Thoughts for two Hours,
or more, with such Violence, that it set my very Blood into a Ferment, and my Pulse beat as high as if I had been
in a Feaver, meerly with the extraordinary Fervour of my
Mind about it; Nature, as if I had been fatigued and exhausted with the very Thought of it, threw me into a
sound Sleep; one would have thought, I should have
dream'd of it: But I did not, nor of any Thing relating to
it; but I dream'd, that as I was going out in the Morning
as usual from my Castle, I saw upon the Shore, two *Canoes*, and eleven Savages coming to Land, and that they
brought with them another Savage, who they were going
to kill, in Order to eat him; when on a sudden, the Savage
that they were going to kill, jumpt away, and ran for his
Life; and I thought in my Sleep, that he came running
into my little thick Grove, before my Fortification, to
hide himself; and that I seeing him alone, and not perceiving that the other sought him that Way, show'd my
self to him, and smiling upon him, encourag'd him; that
he kneel'd down to me, seeming to pray me to assist him;
upon which I shew'd my Ladder, made him go up, and
carry'd him into my Cave, and he became my Servant;
and that as soon as I had gotten this Man, I said to my
self, now I may certainly venture to the main Land; for
this Fellow will serve me as a Pilot, and will tell me what
to do, and whether to go for Provisions; and whether not
to go for fear of being devoured, what Places to venture

into, and what to escape: I wak'd with this Thought, and was under such inexpressible Impressions of Joy, at the Prospect of my Escape in my Dream, that the Disappointments which I felt upon coming to my self, and finding it was no more than a Dream, were equally extravagant the other Way, and threw me into a very great Dejection of Spirit.

Upon this however, I made this Conclusion, that my only Way to go about an Attempt for an Escape, was, if possible, to get a Savage into my Possession; and if possible, it should be one of their Prisoners, who they had condemn'd to be eaten, and should bring thither to kill; but these Thoughts still were attended with this Difficulty, that it was impossible to effect this, without attacking a whole Caravan of them, and killing them all; and this was not only a very desperate Attempt, and might miscarry; but on the other Hand, I had greatly scrupled the Lawfulness of it to me; and my Heart trembled at the thoughts of shedding so much Blood, tho' it was for my Deliverance. I need not repeat the Arguments which occurr'd to me against this, they being the same mention'd before; but tho' I had other Reasons to offer now (*viz.*) that those Men were Enemies to my Life, and would devour me, if they could; that it was Self-preservation in the highest Degree, to deliver my self from this Death of a Life, and was acting in my own Defence, as much as if they were actually assaulting me, and the like. I say, tho' these Things argued for it, yet the Thoughts of shedding Humane Blood for my Deliverance, were very Terrible to me, and such as I could by no Means reconcile my self to, a great while

However, at last, after many secret Disputes with my self, and after great Perplexities about it, for all these

Arguments one Way and another struggl'd in my Head a long Time, the eager prevailing Desire of Deliverance at length master'd all the rest; and I resolved, if possible, to get one of those Savages into my Hands, cost what it would. My next Thing then was to contrive how to do it, and this indeed was very difficult to resolve on: But as I could pitch upon no probable Means for it, so I resolv'd to put my self upon the Watch, to see them when they came on Shore, and leave the rest to the Event, taking such Measures as the Opportunity should present, let be what would be.

With these Resolutions in my Thoughts, I set my self upon the Scout, as often as possible, and indeed so often till I was heartily tir'd of it, for it was above a Year and a Half that I waited, and for great part of that Time went out to the *West* End, and to the *South West* Corner of the Island, almost every Day, to see for Canoes, but none appear'd. This was very discouraging, and began to trouble me much, tho' I cannot say that it did in this Case, as it had done some time before that, (*viz.*) wear off the Edge of my Desire to the Thing. But the longer it seem'd to be delay'd, the more eager I was for it; in a Word, I was not at first so careful to shun the sight of these Savages, and avoid being seen by them, as I was now eager to be upon them.

Besides, I fancied my self able to manage One, nay, Two or Three Savages, if I had them, so as to make them entirely Slaves to me, to do whatever I should direct them, and to prevent their being able at any time to do me any Hurt. It was a great while, that I pleas'd my self with this Affair, but nothing still presented; all my Fancies and Schemes came to nothing, for no Savages came near me for a great while.

About a Year and half after I had entertain'd these Notions, and by long musing, had as it were resolved them all into nothing, for want of an Occasion to put them in Execution, I was surpriz'd one Morning early, with seeing no less than five *canoes* all on Shore together on my side the Island; and the People who belong'd to them all landed, and out of my sight: The Number of them broke all my Measures, for seeing so many, and knowing that they always came four or six, or sometimes more in a Boat, I could not tell what to think of it, or how to take my Measures, to attack Twenty or Thirty Men single handed; so I lay still in my Castle, perplex'd and discomforted: However I put my self into all the same Postures for an Attack that I had formerly provided, and was just ready for Action, if any Thing had presented; having waited a good while, listening to hear if they made any Noise; at length being very impatient, I set my Guns at the Foot of my Ladder, and clamber'd up to the Top of the Hill, by my two Stages as usual; standing so however that my Head did not appear above the Hill, so that they could not perceive me by any Means; here I observ'd by the help of my Perspective Glass, that they were no less than Thirty in Number, that they had a Fire kindled, that they had had Meat dress'd. How they had cook'd it, that I knew not, or what it was; but they were all Dancing in I know not how many barbarous Gestures and Figures, their own Way, round the Fire.

While I was thus looking on them, I perceived by my Perspective, two miserable Wretches dragg'd from the Boats, where it seems they were laid by, and were now brought out for the Slaughter. I perceived one of them immediately fell, being knock'd down, I suppose with a Club or Wooden Sword, for that was their way, and two or three others were at work immediately cutting him open for their Cookery, while the other Victim was left standing by himself, till they should be ready for him. In that very Moment this poor Wretch seeing himself a little at Liberty, Nature inspir'd him with Hopes of Life, and he started away from them, and ran with incredible Swiftness along the Sands directly towards me, I mean towards that part of the Coast, where my Habitation was.

I was dreadfully frighted, (that I must acknowledge) when I perceived him to run my Way; and especially, when as I thought I saw him pursued by the whole Body, and now I expected that part of my Dream was coming to pass, and that he would certainly take shelter in my Grove; but I could not depend by any means upon my Dream for the rest of it, (*viz.*) that the other Savages would not pursue him thither, and find him there. However I kept my Station, and my Spirits began to recover, when I found that there was not above three Men that follow'd him, and still more was I encourag'd, when I found that he outstrip'd them exceedingly in running, and gain'd Ground of them, so that if he could but hold it for half an Hour, I saw easily he would fairly get away from them all.

There was between them and my Castle, the Creek which I mention'd often at the first part of my Story, when I landed my Cargoes out of the Ship; and this I saw plainly, he must necessarily swim over, or the poor Wretch would be taken there: But when the Savage escaping came thither, he made nothing of it, tho' the Tide was then up, but plunging in, swam thro' in about Thirty Strokes or thereabouts, landed and ran on with exceeding Strength and Swiftness; when the Three Persons came to the Creek, I found that Two of them could Swim, but the Third cou'd not, and that standing on the

R. Crusoe rescues his Man Friday and Kills his Pursuers

other Side, he look'd at the other, but went no further; and soon after went softly back again, which as it happen'd, was very well for him in the main.

I observ'd, that the two who swam, were yet more than twice as long swimming over the Creek, as the Fellow was, that fled from them: It came now very warmly upon my Thoughts, and indeed irresistibly, that now was my Time to get me a Servant, and perhaps a Companion, or Assistant; and that I was call'd plainly by Providence to save this poor Creature's Life; I immediately run down the Ladders with all possible Expedition, fetch'd my two Guns, for they were both but at the Foot of the Ladders, as I observ'd above; and getting up again, with the same haste, to the Top of the Hill, I cross'd toward the Sea; and having a very short Cut, and all down Hill, clapp'd my self in the way, between the Pursuers, and the Pursu'd; hallowing aloud to him that fled, who looking back, was at first perhaps as much frighted at me, as at them; but I beckon'd with my Hand to him, to come back; and in the mean time, I slowly advanc'd towards the two that follow'd; then rushing at once upon the foremost, I knock'd him down with the Stock of my Piece; I was loath to fire, because I would not have the rest hear; though at that distance, it would not have been easily heard, and being out of Sight of the Smoke too, they wou'd not have easily known what to make of it: Having knock'd this Fellow down, the other who pursu'd with him stopp'd, as if he had been frighted; and I advanc'd a-pace towards him; but as I came nearer, I perceiv'd presently, he had a Bow and Arrow, and was fitting it to shoot at me; so I was then necessitated to shoot at him first, which I did, and kill'd him at the first Shoot; the poor Savage who fled, but had stopp'd; though he saw both his Enemies fallen, and kill'd, as he thought; yet was so frighted with the Fire, and Noise of my Piece; that he ſtood Stock ſtill, and neither came forward or went backward, tho' he seem'd rather enclin'd to fly ſtill, than to come on; I hollow'd again to him, and made Signs to come forward, which he easily underſtood, and came a little way, then ſtopp'd again, and then a little further, and ſtopp'd again, and I cou'd then perceive that he ſtood trembling, as if he had been taken Prisoner, and had juſt been to be kill'd, as his two Enemies were. I beckon'd him again to come to me, and gave him all the Signs of Encouragement that I could think of, and he came nearer and nearer, kneeling down every Ten or Twelve ſteps in token of acknowledgement for my saving his Life: I smil'd at him, and look'd pleasantly, and beckon'd to him to come ſtill nearer; at length he came close to me, and then he kneel'd down again, kiss'd the Ground, and laid his Head upon the Ground, and taking me by the Foot, set my Foot upon his Head; this it seems was in token of swearing to be my Slave for ever; I took him up, and made much of him, and encourag'd him all I could. But there was more work to do yet, for I perceived the Savage who I knock'd down, was not kill'd, but ſtunn'd with the blow, and began to come to himself; so I pointed to him, and showing him the Savage, that he was not dead; upon this he spoke some Words to me, and though I could not underſtand them, yet I thought they were pleasant to hear, for they were the firſt sound of a Man's Voice, that I had heard, *my own excepted*, for above Twenty Five Years. But there was no time for such Refleƈtions now, the Savage who was knock'd down recover'd himself so far, as to sit up upon the Ground, and I perceived that my Savage began to be afraid; but when

I saw that, I presented my other Piece at the Man, as if I would shoot him, upon this my Savage, *for so I call him now*, made a Motion to me to lend him my Sword, which hung naked in a Belt by my side; so I did: he no sooner had it, but he runs to his Enemy, and at one blow cut off his Head as cleaverly, no Executioner in *Germany* could have done it sooner or better; which I thought very strange, for one who I had Reason to believe never saw a Sword in his Life before, except their own Wooden Swords; however it seems, as I learn'd afterwards, they make their Wooden Swords so sharp, so heavy, and the Wood is so hard, that they will cut off Heads even with them, ay and Arms, and that at one blow too; when he had done this, he comes laughing to me in Sign of Triumph, and brought me the Sword again, and with Abundance of Gestures which I did not understand, laid it down with the Head of the Savage, that he had kill'd just before me.

But that which astonish'd him most, was to know how I had kill'd the other Indian so far off, so pointing to him, he made Signs to me to let him go to him, so I bad him go, as well as I could; when he came to him, he stood like one amaz'd, looking at him, turn'd him first on one side, then on t'other, look'd at the Wound the Bullet had made, which it seems was just in his Breast, where it had made a Hole, and no great Quantity of Blood had follow'd, but he had bled inwardly, for he was quite dead; He took up his Bow, and Arrows, and came back, so I turn'd to go away, and beckon'd to him to follow me, making Signs to him, that more might come after them.

Upon this he sign'd to me, that he should bury them with Sand, that they might not be seen by the rest if they follow'd; and so I made Signs again to him to do so; he fell to Work, and in an instant he had scrap'd a Hole in the Sand, with his Hands, big enough to bury the first in, and then dragg'd him into it, and cover'd him, and did so also by the other; I believe he had bury'd them both in a Quarter of an Hour; then calling him away, I carry'd him not to my Castle, but quite away to my Cave, on the farther Part of the Island; so I did not let my Dream come to pass in that Part. *viz.* That he came into my Grove for shelter.

Here I gave him Bread, and a Bunch of Raisins to eat, and a Draught of Water, which I found he was indeed in great Distress for, by his Running; and having refresh'd him, I made Signs for him to go lie down and sleep; pointing to a Place where I had laid a great Parcel of Rice Straw, and a Blanket upon it, which I used to sleep upon my self sometimes; so the poor Creature laid down, and went to sleep.

He was a comely handsome Fellow, perfectly well made; with straight strong Limbs, not too large; tall and well shap'd, and as I reckon, about twenty six Years of Age. He had a very good Countenance, not a fierce and surly Aspect; but seem'd to have something very manly in his Face, and yet he had all the Sweetness and Softness of an *European* in his Countenance too, especially when he smil'd. His Hair was long and black, not curl'd like Wool; his Forehead very high, and large, and a great Vivacity and sparkling Sharpness in his Eyes. The Colour of his Skin was not quite black, but very tawny; and yet not of an ugly yellow nauseous tawny, as the *Brasilians*, and *Virginians*, and other Natives of *America* are; but of a bright kind of a dun olive Colour, that had in it something very agreeable; tho' not very easy to describe. His Face was round, and plump; his Nose small, not flat like

the Negroes, a very good Mouth, thin Lips, and his fine
Teeth well set, and white as Ivory. After he had slum-
ber'd, rather than slept, about half an Hour, he wak'd
again, and comes out of the Cave to me; for I had been
milking my Goats, which I had in the Enclosure just by:
When he espy'd me, he came running to me, laying himself down again upon the Ground, with all the possible
Signs of an humble thankful Disposition, making a many
antick Gestures to show it: At last he lays his Head flat
upon the Ground, close to my Foot, and sets my other
Foot upon his Head, as he had done before; and after
this, made all the Signs to me of Subjection, Servitude,
and Submission imaginable, to let me know, how he
would serve me as long as he liv'd. I understood him in
many Things, and let him know, I was very well pleas'd
with him; in a little Time I began to speak to him, and
teach him to speak to me; and first, I made him know his
Name should be *Friday*, which was the Day I sav'd his
Life; I call'd him so for the Memory of the Time; I likewise taught him to say *Master*, and then let him know,
that was to be my Name; I likewise taught him to say,
Y ES, and N o, and to know the Meaning of them; I
gave him some Milk, in an earthen Pot, and let him see
me Drink it before him, and sop my Bread in it; and I
gave him a Cake of Bread, to do the like, which he quickly comply'd with, and made Signs that it was very good
for him.

I kept there with him all that Night; but as soon as it
was Day, I beckon'd to him to come with me, and let him
know, I would give him some Cloaths, at which he seem'd
very glad, for he was stark naked: As we went by the
Place where he had bury'd the two Men, he pointed exactly to the Place, and shew'd me the Marks that he had

made to find them again, making Signs to me, that we should dig them up again, and eat them; at this I appear'd very angry, express'd my Abhorrence of it, made as if I would vomit at the Thoughts of it, and beckon'd with my Hand to him to come away, which he did immediately, with great Submission. I then led him up to the Top of the Hill, to see if his Enemies were gone; and pulling out my Glass, I look'd, and saw plainly the Place where they had been, but no appearance of them, or of their *Canoes*; so that it was plain they were gone, and had left their two Comrades behind them, without any search after them.

But I was not content with this Discovery; but having now more Courage, and consequently more Curiosity, I took my Man *Friday* with me, giving him the Sword in his Hand, with the Bow and Arrows at his Back, which I found he could use very dextrously, making him carry one Gun for me, and I two for my self, and away we march'd to the Place, where these Creatures had been; for I had a Mind now to get some fuller Intelligence of them: When I came to the Place, my very Blood ran chill in my Veins, and my Heart sunk within me, at the Horror of the Spectacle: Indeed it was a dreadful Sight, at least it was so to me; though *Friday* made nothing of it: The Place was cover'd with humane Bones, the Ground dy'd with their Blood, great Pieces of Flesh left here and there, half eaten, mangl'd and scorch'd; and in short, all the Tokens of the triumphant Feast they had been making there, after a Victory over their Enemies. I saw three Skulls, five Hands, and the Bones of three or four Legs and Feet, and abundance of other Parts of the Bodies; and *Friday*, by his Signs, made me understand, that they brought over four Prisoners to feast upon; that three of them were eaten up, and that he, pointing to himself, was the fourth: That there had been a great Battle between them, and their next King, whose Subjects it seems he had been one of; and that they had taken a great Number of Prisoners, all which were carry'd to several Places by those that had taken them in the Fight, in order to feast upon them, as was done here by these Wretches upon those they brought hither.

I caus'd *Friday* to gather all the Skulls, Bones, Flesh, and whatever remain'd, and lay them together on a Heap, and make a great Fire upon it, and burn them all to Ashes: I found *Friday* had still a hankering Stomach after some of the Flesh, and was still a Cannibal in his Nature; but I discover'd so much Abhorrence at the very Thoughts of it, and at the least Appearance of it, that he durst not discover it; for I had by some Means let him know, that I would kill him if he offer'd it.

When we had done this, we came back to our Castle, and there I fell to work for my Man *Friday*; and first of all, I gave him a pair of Linnen Drawers, which I had out of the poor Gunner's Chest I mentioned, and which I found in the Wreck; and which with a little Alteration fitted him very well; then I made him a Jerkin of Goat's-skin, as well as my Skill would allow; and I was now grown a tollerable good Taylor; and I gave him a Cap, which I had made of a Hare-skin, very convenient, and fashionable enough; and thus he was cloath'd for the present, tollerably well; and was mighty well pleas'd to see himself almost as well cloath'd as his Master: It is true, he went awkwardly in these Things at first; wearing the Drawers was very awkard to him, and the Sleeves of the Wastcoat gall'd his Shoulders, and the inside of his Arms; but a little easing them where he complain'd they hurt him, and using himself to them, at length he took to them very well.

The next Day after I came home to my Hutch with him, I began to consider where I should lodge him, and that I might do well for him, and yet be perfectly easy my self, I made a little Tent for him in the vacant Place between my two Fortifications, in the inside of the laſt, and in the outside of the firſt; and as there was a Door, or Entrance there into my Cave, I made a formal fram'd Door Case, and a Door to it of Boards, and set it up in the Passage, a little within the Entrance; and causing the Door to open on the inside, I barr'd it up in the Night, taking in my Ladders too; so that *Friday* could no way come at me in the inside of my innermoſt wall, without making so much Noise in getting over, that it muſt needs waken me; for my firſt Wall had now a compleat Roof over it of long Poles, covering all my Tent, and leaning up to the side of the Hill, which was again laid cross with smaller Sticks inſtead of Laths, and then thatch'd over a great Thickness, with the Rice Straw, which was ſtrong like Reeds; and at the Hole or Place which was left to go in or out by the Ladder, I had plac'd a kind of Trap-door, which if it had been attempted on the outside, would not have open'd at all, but would have fallen down, and made a great Noise; and as to Weapons, I took them all in to my Side every Night.

But I needed none of all this Precaution; for never Man had a more faithful, loving, sincere Servant, than *Friday* was to me; without Passions, Sullenness or Designs, perfectly oblig'd and engag'd; his very Affections were ty'd to me, like those of a Child to a Father; and I dare say, he would have sacrific'd his Life for the saving mine upon any occasion whatsoever; the many Teſti-

˙monies he gave me of this, put it out of doubt, and soon convinc'd me, that I needed to use no Precautions as to my Safety on his Account.

This frequently gave me occasion to observe, and that with wonder, that however it had pleas'd God, in his Providence, and in the Government of the Works of his Hands, to take from so great a Part of the World of his Creatures, the beſt Uses to which their Faculties, and the Powers of their Souls are adapted; yet that he has be-ſtow'd upon them the same Powers, the same Reason, the same Affeḉtions, the same Sentiments of Kindness and Obligation, the same Passions and Resentments of Wrongs; the same Sense of Gratitude, Sincerity, Fideli-ty, and all the Capacities of doing Good, and receiving Good, that he has given to us; and that when he pleases to offer to them Occasions of exerting these, they are as ready, nay, more ready to apply them to the right Uses for which they were beſtow'd, than we are: and this made me very melancholly sometimes, in reflecting as the seve-ral Occasions presented, how mean a Use we make of all these, even though we have these Powers enlighten'd by the great Lamp of Inſtruḉtion, the Spirit of God, and by the Knowledge of his Word, added to our Underſtand-ing; and why it has pleas'd God to hide the like saving Knowledge from so many Millions of Souls, who if I might judge by this poor Savage, would make a much better use of it than we did.

From hence, I sometimes was led too far to invade the Soverainty of *Providence*, and as it were arraign the Jus-tice of so arbitrary a Disposition of Things, that should hide that Light from some, and reveal it to others, and yet expeḉt a like Duty from both: But I shut it up, and check'd my Thoughts with this Conclusion, (1ſt.) That we did not know by what Light and Law these should be Condemn'd; but that as God was necessarily, and by the Nature of his Being, infinitely Holy and Juſt, so it could not be, but that if these Creatures were all sentenc'd to Absence from himself, it was on account of sinning againſt that Light which, as the Scripture says, was a Law to themselves, and by such Rules as their Consciences would acknowledge to be juſt, tho' the Foundation was not discover'd to us: And (2d.) that ſtill as we are all the Clay in the Hand of the Potter, no Vessel could say to him, Why haſt thou form'd me thus?

But to return to my New Companion; I was greatly delighted with him, and made it my Business to teach him every Thing, that was proper to make him useful, handy, and helpful; but especially to make him speak, and underſtand me when I spake, and he was the apteſt Schollar that ever was, and particularly was so merry, so conſtantly diligent, and so pleas'd, when he cou'd but underſtand me, or make me underſtand him, that it was very pleasant to me to talk to him; and now my Life began to be so easy, that I began to say to my self, that could I but have been safe from more Savages, I cared not, if I was never to remove from the place while I lived.

After I had been two or three Days return'd to my Castle, I thought that, in order to bring *Friday* off from his horrid way of feeding, and from the Relish of a Cannibal's Stomach, I ought to let him taſte other Flesh; so I took him out with me one Morning to the Woods—I went indeed intending to kill a Kid out of my own Flock, and bring him home and dress it. But as I was going, I saw a She Goat lying down in the Shade, and two young Kids sitting by her. I catch'd hold of *Friday*, hold says I, ſtand ſtill; and made Signs to him not to ſtir, immediate-

ly I presented my Piece, shot and kill'd one of the Kids.
The poor Creature who had at a Distance indeed seen me
kill the Savage his Enemy, but did not know, or could
imagine how it was done, was sensibly surpriz'd trembled, and shook, and look'd so amaz'd, that I thought he
would have sunk down. He did not see the Kid I shot at,
or perceive I had kill'd it, but ripp'd up his Waistcoat to
feel if he was not wounded, and as I found, presently
thought I was resolv'd to kill him; for he came and kneel'd
down to me, and embraceing my Knees, said a great
many Things I did not understand; but I could easily see
that the meaning was to pray me not to kill him.

I soon found a way to convince him that I would do
him no harm, and taking him up by the Hand laugh'd at
him, and pointed to the Kid which I had kill'd, beckoned
to him to run and fetch it, which he did; and while he was
wondering and looking to see how the Creature was
kill'd, I loaded my Gun again, and by and by I saw a great
Fowl like a Hawk sit upon a Tree within Shot; so to let
Friday understand a little what I would do, I call'd him to
me again, pointed at the Fowl which was indeed a Parrot,
tho' I thought it had been a Hawk, I say pointing to the
Parrot, and to my Gun, and to the Ground under the Parrot, to let him see I would make it fall, I made him understand that I would shoot and kill that Bird; according I
fir'd and bad him look, and immediately he saw the Parrot fall, he stood like one frighted again, notwithstanding
all I had said to him; and I found he was the more amaz'd
because he did not see me put any Thing into the Gun;
but thought that there must be some wonderful Fund of
Death and Destruction in that Thing, able to kill Man,
Beast, Bird, or any Thing near, or far off, and the Astonishment this created in him was such, as could not wear

off for a long Time; and I believe, if I would have let him, he would have worshipp'd me and my Gun: As for the Gun it self, he would not so much as touch it for several Days after; but would speak to it, and talk to it, as if it had answer'd him, when he was by himself; which, as I afterwards learn'd of him, was to desire it not to kill him.

Well, after his Aſtonishment was a little over at this, I pointed to him to run and fetch the Bird I had shot, which he did, but ſtay'd some Time; for the Parrot not being quite dead, was flutter'd away a good way off from the Place where she fell; however, he found her, took her up, and brought her to me; and as I had perceiv'd his Ignorance about the Gun before, I took this Advantage to charge the Gun again, and not let him see me do it, that I might be ready for any other Mark that might present; but nothing more offer'd at that Time; so I brought home the Kid, and the same Evening I took the Skin off, and cut it out as well as I could; and having a Pot for that purpose, I boil'd, or ſtew'd some of the Flesh, and made some very good Broth; and after I had begun to eat some, I gave some to my Man, who seem'd very glad of it, and lik'd it very well; but that which was ſtrangeſt to him, was, to see me eat Salt with it; he made a Sign to me, that the Salt was not good to eat, and putting a little into his own Mouth, he seem'd to nauseate it, and would spit and sputter at it, washing his Mouth with fresh Water after it; on the other hand, I took some Meat in my Mouth without Salt, and I pretended to spit and sputter for want of Salt, as faſt as he had done at the Salt; but it would not do, he would never care for Salt with his Meat, or in his Broth; at leaſt not a great while, and then but a very little.

Having thus fed him with boil'd Meat and Broth, I was resolv'd to feaſt him the next Day with roaſting a

Piece of the Kid; this I did by hanging it before the Fire, in a String, as I had seen many People do in *England*, setting two Poles up, one on each side the Fire, and one cross on the Top, and tying the String to the Cross-ſtick, letting the Meat turn continually: This *Friday* admir'd very much; but when he came to taſte the Flesh, he took so many ways to tell me how well he lik'd it, that I could not but underſtand him; and at laſt he told me he would never eat Man's flesh any more, which I was very glad to hear.

The next Day I set him to work to beating some Corn out, and sifting it in the manner I us'd to do, as I obſerv'd before, and he soon underſtood how to do it as well as I, especially after he had seen what the Meaning of it was, and that it was to make Bread of; for after that I let him see me make my Bread, and bake it too, and in a little Time *Friday* was able to do all the Work for me, as well as I could do it my self.

I begun now to consider, that having two Mouths to feed, inſtead of one, I muſt provide more Ground for my Harveſt, and plant a larger Quantity of Corn, than I us'd to do; so I mark'd out a larger Piece of Land, and began the Fence in the same Manner as before, in which *Friday* not only work'd very willingly, and very hard; but did it very chearfully, and I told him what it was for; that it was for Corn to make more Bread, because he was now with me, and that I might have enough for him, and my self too: He appear'd very sensible of that Part, and let me know, that he thought I had much more Labour upon me on his Account, than I had for my self; and that he would work the harder for me, if I would tell him what to do.

This was the pleasanteſt Year of all the Life I led in

248 Life & Adventures of ROBINSON CRUSOE

this Place; *Friday* began to talk pretty well, and under-stand the Names of almost every Thing I had occasion to call for, and of every Place I had to send him to, and talk'd a great deal to me; so that in short I began now to have some Use for my Tongue again, which indeed I had very little occasion for before; that is to say, *about Speech;* besides the Pleasures of talking to him, I had a singular Satisfaction in the Fellow himself; his simple unfeign'd Honesty, appear'd to me more and more every Day, and I began really to love the Creature; and on his Side, I be-lieve he lov'd me more than it was possible for him ever to love any Thing before.

I had a Mind once to try if he had any hankering Incli-nation to his own Country again, and having learn'd him *English* so well that he could answer me almost any Ques-tions, I ask'd him whether the Nation that he belong'd to never conquer'd in Battle, at which he smil'd; and said; yes, yes, we always fight the better; that is, he meant al-ways get the better in Fight; and so we began the follow-ing Discourse: You always fight the better, said I, How came you to be taken Prisoner then, *Friday?*

Friday, My Nation beat much, for all that.

Master, How beat; if your Nation beat them, how came you to be taken?

Friday, They more many than my Nation in the Place where me was; they take one, two, three, and me; my Nation over-beat them in the yonder Place, where me no was; there my Nation take one, two, great Thousand.

Master, But why did not your Side recover you from the Hands of your Enemies then?

Friday, They run one, two, three, and me, and make go in the *Canoe;* my Nation have no *Canoe* that time.

Master, Well, *Friday,* and What does your Nation do

with the Men they take, do they carry them away, and eat them, as these did?

Friday, Yes, my Nation eat Mans too, eat all up.

Master, Where do they carry them?

Friday, Go to other Place where they think.

Master, Do they come hither?

Friday, Yes, yes, they come hither; come other else Place.

Master, Have you been here with them?

Friday, Yes, I been here; [*points to the* N.W. *Side of the Island, which, it seems, was their Side.*]

By this I understood, that my Man *Friday* had formerly been among the Savages, who us'd to come on Shore on the farther Part of the Island, on the same Man eating Occasions that he was now brought for; and sometime after, when I took the Courage to carry him to that Side, being the same I formerly mention'd, he presently knew the Place, and told me, he was there once when they eat up twenty Men, two Women, and one Child; he could not tell Twenty in *English*; but he numbred them by laying so many Stones on a Row, and pointing to me to tell them over.

I have told this Passage, because it introduces what follows; that after I had had this Discourse with him, I ask'd him how far it was from our Island to the Shore, and whether the *Canoes* were not often lost; he told me, there was no Danger, no *Canoes* ever lost; but that after a little way out to the Sea, there was a Current, and Wind, always one way in the Morning, the other in the Afternoon.

This I understood to be no more than the Sets of the Tide, as going out, or coming in; but I afterwards understood, it was occasion'd by the great Draft and Reflux of the mighty River *Oroonooko*; in the Mouth, or the Gulph of which River, as I found afterwards, our Island lay; and this Land which I perceiv'd to the *W.* and *N.W.* was the great Island *Trinidad*, on the *North* Point of the Mouth of the River: I ask'd *Friday* a thousand Queſtions about the Country, the Inhabitants, the Sea, the Coaſt, and what Nations were near; he told me all he knew with the greateſt Openness imaginable; I ask'd him the Name of the several Nations of his Sort of People; but could get no other Name than *Caribs*; from whence I easily underſtood, that these were the *Caribbees*, which our Maps place on the Part of *America*, which reaches from the Mouth of the River *Oroonooko* to *Guiana*, and onwards to *St. Martha*: He told me that up a great way beyond the Moon, that was, beyond the Setting of the Moon, which muſt be *W.* from their Country, there dwelt white bearded Men, like me; and pointed to my great Whiskers, which I mention'd before; and that they had kill'd *much Mans*, that was his Word; by all which I underſtood, he meant the *Spaniards*, whose Cruelties in *America* had been spread over the whole Countries, and was remember'd by all the Nations from Father to Son.

I enquir'd if he could tell me how I might come from this Island, and get among those white Men; he told me, yes, yes, I might go *in two Canoe*; I could not underſtand what he meant, or make him describe to me what he meant by *two Canoe*, till at laſt with great Difficulty, I found he meant it muſt be in a large great Boat, as big as *two Canoes*.

This Part of *Friday*'s Discourse began to relish with me very well, and from this Time I entertain'd some Hopes, that one Time or other, I might find an Opportunity to make my Escape from this Place; and that this poor Savage might be a Means to help me to do it.

END OF VOLUME I